THE MAN WHO WAS FRANKENSTEIN

The Giant Insect Strikes! — *a dramatic illustration by Philip Baynes for F. H. Power's story 'The Electric Vampire' which was based on Andrew Crosse's experiments. It appeared in* The London Magazine, *October 1910.*

THE MAN WHO WAS FRANKENSTEIN

PETER HAINING

FREDERICK MULLER LIMITED
LONDON

First published in Great Britain 1979
by Frederick Muller Limited, London NW2 6LE

Haining, Peter
  The man who was Frankenstein.
  1. Crosse, Andrew 2. Scientists – England
  – Biography
  I. Title
  509'.2'4   QJ43.C/
  ISBN–0–584–10356–5

Typeset by Computacomp (UK) Ltd, Fort William, Scotland, and
Printed in Great Britain by Billing & Sons Ltd, Guildford, London
and Worcester.

Contents

Illustrations

For
PAM AND JOE CHAMBERLAINE
Who went with me in search of Andrew Crosse

Preface

There has been much discussion and many theories advanced as to how nineteen-year-old Mary Shelley got her inspiration in 1816 to write *Frankenstein or The Modern Prometheus*, beyond dispute the greatest of all horror novels, a classic of literature and probably the most filmed of all stories (at least 25 times). It has been said it was born in a particularly terrible nightmare; in the experiments into Galvanism — the science of animating the dead — which were taking place at the beginning of the nineteenth century; and in the fascination her lover, the poet Percy Bysshe Shelley, had for electricity.

I believe it is probable that all these elements played a part in exciting Mary's imagination. However, I also believe there was a *real person* she had seen and heard lecture about his pioneer experiments in electricity — a man who was called a wizard and was said to be in league with the Devil; a man almost hounded from his isolated country home where he performed fantastic experiments which lit up the skies for miles around with flashes of light and sounds like the din of hell; a man who was later to astound science and horrify the world by seemingly creating life from inanimate objects.

The man was Andrew Crosse — and this is his story.

The neighbours of Andrew Crosse regarded him as more devil than man. They did not understand the bright flashes that lighted his laboratory windows at night when he was tinkering with his crude electrical devices. Not only was he dreaded and shunned as 'the thunder and lightning man', but he was denounced as an atheist, a blasphemer, and a Frankenstein who had best be put in chains for the common safety. Andrew Crosse minded his own business, it is true, but his was a very strange business for the early 1800's. And one of his experiments remains a very strange business to this day.

Frank Edwards
Stranger Than Science, 1959.

Today we look back on Crosse's story as one of the great enigmas of history, a problem still unsolved, still debated by learned scientists the world over. Was this gentleman-scientist, this amateur electrician, in fact a forerunner of Frankenstein?

Valentine Dyall
Unsolved Mysteries, 1954.

1

'The Wizard of the Quantocks'

It is early evening, and the big, sprawling mansion lies dark and still against the backdrop of rolling hills. Rain is beginning to fall and there is a wind that moans eerily through the cluster of tall trees. Between them, lines of copper wires sway gently in the breeze, all woven like some giant spider's web which converges on a solitary window on the south wall of the building. A light is glowing dimly in the room.

Inside, in a high arched room, row upon row of bottles, jars and tubes line the walls. Many of these vessels are full of multi-coloured liquids; others with strange-looking compounds of crystals or chemicals bubbling silently. Above, the copper wires from outside converge on an odd-looking piece of equipment, somehow like a giant battery, which occasionally gives off a humming sound. To the curious observer it is a place that suggests strange experiments with the very forces of nature itself ...

But you are startled in the midst of your observations, by the smart crackling sound that attends the passage of an electrical spark; you hear also the rumbling of distant thunder. The rain is already splashing in great drops against the glass, and the sound of the passing sparks continues to startle your ear.

Your host is in high glee, for a battery of electricity is about to come within his reach a thousand-fold more powerful than all

1

those in the room strung together. You follow his hasty steps to the organ gallery, and curiously approach the spot whence the noise proceeds that has attracted your notice.

You see at the window a huge brass conductor, with a discharging rod near it passing into the floor, and from the one knob to the other, sparks are leaping with increasing rapidity and noise, rap, rap, rap — bang, bang, bang; you are afraid to approach near this terrible engine, and well you may; for every spark that passes would kill twenty men at one blow, if they were linked together hand in hand, and the spark sent through the circle.

Almost trembling, you note that from this conductor wires pass off without the window, and the electric fluid is conducted harmlessly away. On the instrument itself is inscribed in large letters the warning words,

Noli me tangere.

Nevertheless, your host does not fear. He approaches as boldly as if the flowing stream of fire were a harmless spark. Armed with his insulated rod, he plays with the mighty power; he directs it where he will; he sends it into his batteries: having charged them thus, he shows you how wire is melted, dissipated in a moment, by its passage; how metals — silver, gold, and tin — are inflamed, and burn like paper, only with most brilliant hues.

He shows you a mimic aurora, and a falling star, and so proves to you the cause of those beautiful phenomena; and then he tells you that the wires you had noticed, as passing from tree to tree round the grounds, were connected with the conductor before you; that they collected the electricity of the atmosphere as it floated by, and brought it into the room in the shape of the sparks that you had witnessed with such awe.

And then, perhaps, he will tell you that the electricity lies in a thunder-cloud in zones, alternately positive and negative, and he will add that he is able at all times thus to measure the electrical state of the atmosphere; and he will tell you many curious facts which he has subsequently observed relative to that state at various periods of the day and night, and at the different seasons of the year ...

The reader can be forgiven for thinking he has just been reading some passages from the most famous of all horror novels, Mary Shelley's *Frankenstein*. For does not her hero draw down the power of the thunderstorm to animate the body of the creature he has made from the corpses of dead men?

In fact, though, the above passages are from an article by one Edward W. Cox, published in the *Taunton Courier* in the autumn of 1836. They describe a visit Cox paid to the home of an amateur scientist and electrician named Andrew Crosse, who lived in an isolated mansion known as Fyne Court in Broomfield, perched high on top of the rolling Quantock Hills. A man, then as now, who was the centre of mystery, speculation and rumour. A man known far and wide as 'The Wizard of the Quantocks' and a man who was on the verge of actually achieving what no scientist before or since has accomplished: the creation of life.

The life and work of Andrew Crosse is one of the great enigmas of science: an episode of electrical experiments which baffled the man who conducted them almost as much as those who heard about them. Nor does the story end there, for this strange man was also a remarkable prophet who predicted years ahead of their time several developments in electricity that we now take for granted. And perhaps most amazing of all — as I shall set out to prove in this book — he was in part responsible for the creation of the novel, *Frankenstein*, by the example of his experiments.

With such resounding claims to be made about Crosse, it is certainly all the more surprising that so little should have been published about him. This is to a degree due to the fact that he did not keep detailed notes of much of his work, and what he did commit to paper was 'most generally written on loose scraps of paper', according to his second wife, Cornelia, who compiled the only biography of him. And, she adds, 'I know that much has been lost that would have been most valuable.'

With some justification, I believe, Mrs Crosse has also written that 'His fame would have been wider, had he been poor, ambitious or wise in worldly wisdom. He was none of these things.'

So, then, what sort of man was Andrew Crosse? The

3

The only known authentic portrait of Andrew Crosse 'The Man Who Was Frankenstein'.

information that we have about him is scattered through a dozen books, the archives of several museums in London and Somerset, and a thin file of newspaper cuttings. He avoided the limelight and publicity, and even when notoriety found him as a result of the extraordinary incident of the *Acari Crossii*, he did much to play down the matter and refused to respond to the sensational outcries against him.

Yet, his importance was recognised enough for *The Times* to devote a column to him on the one hundredth anniversary of this bizarre event. THE MAN WHO 'MADE' INSECTS read the heading on page 17 of the issue of July 29, 1938, and then more sedately and typical of the 'Thunderer' a sub-heading: 'The Experiments of Andrew Crosse'. I should like to quote a little from this article to give you an idea of what is in store in this book.

> One hundred years ago, science and the Churches were disputing about the work of a quiet Somerset gentleman, well known to and respected by members of the Royal Society and the British Association, who in the process of electrical experiments was alleged to have 'made' insects. Andrew Crosse — the 'electrician', they called him— lived at Fyne Court on the Quantock Hills, six miles from Taunton. He died in 1855 in the room in which he had been born 71 years before.

After going on to describe a number of his successful experiments, the paper notes that his work was written about by, among others, W. H. Preece, who 'lived to become Sir William Preece and to assist Marconi in the development of wireless. As a young student he may possibly have known Crosse.'

The Times then comes to the heart of the matter:

> The 'creation' of 'insects' by Crosse was achieved in 1837 when the electrician was 53 years old. He had been producing crystals by passing a current through solutions, and when the 'marvel' occurred he was trying to produce crystals of silica. He took 2 oz. of powdered flint and 6 oz. of potassium carbonate, fused the two in a furnace, reduced the compound again to powder, and then dissolving it in boiling water, slowly added

hydrochloric acid to super-saturation point. With this fluid Crosse saturated a porous stone and then passed his electric current through it. The looked for crystals of silica did not appear, but on the fourteenth day he observed, through a pocket lens, a few small whitish excrescences projecting from the middle of the porous stone. On the eighteenth day these had grown and had thrown out seven or eight filaments. On the twenty-sixth day the filaments assumed the form of perfect 'insects', standing erect on a few bristles which were their 'tails'. On the twenty-eighth day the 'insects' moved their legs and, detaching themselves from the stone, began to travel. In the course of a few weeks 100 of the insects appeared. The smaller had six legs, the larger had eight. Entomologists, examining them, pronounced them to belong to the genus *Acarus* and gave them the title *Acarus Crossi*.

Perhaps not surprisingly, it was some while before the retiring Crosse could bring himself to reveal what had happened: and when he did the story spread from one end of Britain to the other — and in time around the world — creating increasing amazement. Crosse, for his pains, was soon branded as a wizard, a blasphemer, and even an agent of the Devil. He and his house were avoided as if possessed of the plague by the superstitious Somersetshire countrymen. Even other scientists were sceptical of his achievement, though he was able to repeat the creation almost at will. It mattered not the slightest that he did not claim to have 'created' anything.

Only one other national journal that I have been able to trace marked the anniversary, the weekly magazine, *Tit-Bits*, in its issue of September 3, 1938, and perhaps predictably it tended to sensationalise the event in just the way that had originally offended Crosse:

THIS MAN MADE INSECTS!

An English country gentleman puzzled himself by finding something he was not looking for — that which all men can take but no man can give. No man? He, Andrew Crosse, experimental electrician, had done it: he had created life in his own workshop!

Had it happened today instead of in the year 1837 every radio set in the world would have buzzed with the news that in a vessel of liquid on the littered work-bench of a publicity-hating experimenter of Somerset there had appeared live insects whose presence was in direct opposition to all the laws of Nature. For Crosse had accidentally created Life out of a stone. No other explanation was forthcoming to account for the phenomenon.

After detailing the experiments much as *The Times* had done, the magazine concluded:

If the secret of life really had been found it has been lost again this hundred years ... Could Andrew Crosse's achievement be repeated today in the light of today's scientific knowledge combined with enormously improved equipment? The impossible may again happen in some obscure twentieth-century investigator's study — and the creation of Life in the laboratory become an accomplished and awesome fact.

Important though this element is in the story of Andrew Crosse, it is only one facet of the life of an extraordinary man. For Crosse devoted all his energy to exploring the possibilities of electricty and wrote quite early in his life:

Electricity is no longer the paltry confined science which it was once fancied to be, making its appearance only from the friction of glass or wax, employed in childish purposes, serving as a trick for a schoolboy or a nostrum for the quack; but it is even now, though in its infancy, proved to be connected most intimately with all operations in chemistry — with magnetism, with light and caloric, apparently a property belonging to all matter, and perhaps ranging through all space, from sun to sun, from planet to planet, and not improbably the secondary cause of every change in the animal, mineral, vegetable and gaseous systems.

As we shall see through the pages of this book, he sensed the possibilities of electricity long before many of its important developments took place. A story about him I particularly like dates from the year 1816, when he was 32, already the master of Fyne Court, the family ancestral home, and was entertaining a small group of people to dinner. Naturally enough, in his presence the conversation

7

A rather less than accurate picture of Crosse at work from Tit-Bits, September 3, 1938.

focused a good deal on scientific experiments, and electricity in particular. Suddenly he startled his guests with a statement obviously firmly held.

'I prophesy,' he said simply, looking from one face to another around his table, 'that by means of the electric agency we shall be enabled to communicate our thoughts instantaneously with the uttermost ends of the earth.'

The dinner guests were taken aback by such a visionary idea, and though no one would have been so discourteous as to laugh outright at such a claim, privately all of the guests found it very difficult to believe. But every one of

8

them, in fact, lived to see Crosse's prediction come true — the development and use of the electric telegraph.

As a matter of interest, I am always reminded of this story whenever I am in the Broomfield area by the line of electric pylons that straddle the landscape; a mute testimony to Crosse's foresight. His vision is further emphasised by the huge Washford Transmitting Station sited not far away which broadcasts to Wales, and also the giant TV mast on the Mendip Hills serving much of the West of England. I have always thought it particularly appropriate, because of Crosse's work, that nearby Taunton was the first town in the country to have its highways lit by electricity — although in contrast to this, electricity did not reach Broomfield until the 1960s, and the pioneer electrician's home at Fyne Court was not actually connected until 1973!

However, the electric telegraph was not the only prediction which Crosse made about the uses to which the mysterious force of electricity might be put. An early maxim of his was that 'the time is coming when the electric influence will work wonders, and cause an alteration far greater and more permanent than those political convulsions which are now agitating Europe.' A few years later, Crosse was stating, 'I have every reason to believe that the electric action will be universally employed in a vast variety of manufactures over the whole civilised world.'

Among the things he specifically foresaw — and which I shall elaborate on later in this book — were the dry cell battery now used in portable radios, cycle lamps, etc.; the preserving of food by electricity and the stimulation of plant growth through its agency; and perhaps most remarkably of all, the idea of using electric current in the storage of fresh blood so that it might be used again in the future. In a nutshell, for blood transfusions!

Crosse was also something of a literary man and wrote a good deal of poetry which, though nothing special, is still quite readable. His electrical experiments apparently also prompted him to write a short story, 'The Island of Elattosis', which, though uncompleted, can I think be seen as a pioneer piece of Science Fiction.

Crosse's lack of fame was in part due to his own reticence

9

Fyne Court, Broomfield, as it was during Andrew Crosse's time.

All that remains of Fyne Court following the terrible fire. Crosse's laboratory, which survived the blaze, is on the left.

and in part to his desire to live far from the hub of society in London — 'I have a stake through my body which nails me to the Quantocks,' he once said, with a choice of phrase more closely allied to that of the vampire tradition than the scientist.

So now we must address ourselves to the following three questions. Firstly, did an obscure scientist discover the spark of life, a secret still eluding us even though we have conquered much disease, probed the core of the atom and begun the exploration of space? Did he somehow stumble on the mixture of chemicals and electricity which produced living things from lifeless compounds? Secondly, what was the life of this forgotten genius like and did he deserve the calumny and ridicule that was heaped on him? And, thirdly, how did he come to play a part in the creation of one of the greatest characters in literature, Victor Frankenstein, the man who made a dead body come alive?

My search to find the answers was a fascinating and surprising one, which commenced with a journey back to the place where the whole story began — the ruins of Fyne Court, on top of the beautiful rolling Quantock Hills in Somerset ...

2

In Search of a Legend

It seemed a particularly appropriate day when I went for the first time during my research to visit the home of Andrew Crosse. I had set out on a bright winter's afternoon from the charming town of Bridgwater, a thriving community which has retained much of its old character despite the development of considerable local industry. Admittedly, the sunlight was rather watery as I drove out of the town in the direction of Durleigh with the Quantock Hills humped darkly beyond. However, not long after I had passed Durleigh Reservoir and was beginning the start of the climb into the hills through Enmore, the skies were turning decidedly overcast.

I drove on past Enmore and I could not help feeling there would be rain before I reached my final destination. For a moment I was distracted by a curious pseudo-baronial building away to the right: a building of turrets and battlements, just like a Gothic castle. In fact, it seemed almost like something from the set of one of those old horror films of the thirties, and I turned to ask my wife to see if the map she had on her lap could help. Indeed it could: the place was called Enmore Castle. A brief note in the guidebook we had purchased mentioned the place had been built originally in the eighteenth century and had a number of Victorian additions. It was a striking sight.

Now the road began to get steeper and away to the left was what I knew to be an old Roman entrenchment called Ruborough Camp. I had already heard stories about this place: and in particular, the old belief that there was supposed to be a subterranean chamber beneath it filled with a priceless hoard of gold and silver. Many were said to have set out to try and find it, but always the gnomes who guarded it had got the better of them. So 'The Moneyfield', as the rough grassy space was called, had kept its treasure: although the legend had never died thanks to a farm labourer digging up a seal set with a turquoise at the end of the last century, and the discovery of a gold bar not so many years back.

There was no denying that in the fading light of afternoon the place looked eerie. I was reminded of a few lines of verse an old man had told me when I had inquired about the local legends of fairies, pixies and a headless horseman who was supposed to be hereabout:

> There are pixies in the hills of Somerset,
> And the Devil rides apace
> In many a lonely place in Somerset.
> You'd better have a care,
> For witches may be there
> And there's magic in the air in Somerset.

As our climb continued, the skies became more heavy and leaden, and the first spots of rain began to run down the car's windscreen. Away on either side of us lay a carpet of fields, small copses of dark, clustered trees, little groups of farm buildings and occasionally the most extraordinary looking ploughed fields: extraordinary because the colour of the earth was almost blood red. It was quite unlike anything I had seen before, and the strangeness was increased by something that I could see hanging from a stake in one of these fields. It was the corpse of a crow, presumably there to scare off others of its kind.

A bit further along the road we passed an inn named the Traveller's Rest. Although it was closed at this time of day, it was a place we were to visit several times during the course of our research, and in its warm, low-ceilinged interior we were to hear several fascinating stories about Andrew Crosse, the 'thunder and lightning man' as the locals referred to him. One could easily imagine that the inn had changed little in the last couple of centuries, and no doubt during Crosse's time, people walking or coming up in carts from Bridgwater would have been glad to stop here for a drink and a rest before completing the rest of their journey. To be sure, the sign outside of a group of people in a horse-drawn cart being greeted by a publican with a drink in his hand seemed to confirm the impression.

A quarter of a mile on and a signpost pointing to the left indicated Broomfield, the village which was our destination. Now the feeling of getting off the beaten track and away from the bustle of modern life was heightened still further, although we had only come seven miles from Bridgwater.

The climb was steep, the road narrow and barely more than the width of the car. Trees overhung the road and where stretches of earth were visible they had the same look of being like patches of dried blood that we had noticed earlier. A little stream of water which ran down one side of the road, caused by the rain which had fallen earlier in the day, was stained red from contact with this same earth. Occasionally, as we climbed higher, there were sudden openings which gave us spectacular views across the coombs which are a feature of the Quantocks: steep-sided valleys clothed in rough grass and tall coniferous trees.

The rain, which was falling steadily now, pattered through the over-hanging branches of the trees which formed a kind of leafy panoply above us. Once we were forced to pull into a small lay-by when a pony and trap with a couple of passengers came briskly from the opposite direction. The driver was huddled down in his coat, his hands lightly on his animal's reigns, and neither he nor his companion looked up or gave the slightest indication that they were aware of our presence as they passed. The clothing both of them were wearing seemed to belong to a time gone by, and my wife remarked that they probably looked no different to their forebears who had used this same route for generations. Since Andrew Crosse's time, in fact.

We drove on in silence up the narrow, winding lane, until at last the trees fell away and we came to a little cluster of buildings. We had reached Broomfield, the only village to be sited on top of the Quantock Hills — a fact which gave it seclusion, spectacular views, and, when the weather was particularly bad or it snowed, cut it off from the rest of the world.

Records of the village go back to the Domesday Book when it was called Brunfelle, was owned by one William de Mohun, and had a population of 22. Then, as now, it was noted for its woodland and pasture, and at the time of its greatest population, in the 1830s, boasted just over five hundred souls. For a time copper mining went on in the area and there was even an annual fair for coarse cloth and cattle each November 13. Today the number of residents is barely two hundred.

Amidst a small group of cottages we saw one bearing a notice 'The Old Post Office', but there was no sign of a general stores or shop of any other kind. The place seemed quite deserted as we drove through in the direction of the church, but just as we turned a bend an old man hobbled by bent against the rain. It was quite impossible to tell his age, but his figure reminded me of the story we had heard back in Bridgwater, that the people of Broomfield often lived for over a hundred years and more and had a particular liking for cider. Whether the drinking led to longevity no one was quite sure!

There was a profusion of trees everywhere and it was easy to see why it is said the timber in this region is among the best on the Quantocks — Spanish chestnut, oak, elm and fir reaching to great height. Then, when we saw an entrance way shaded by a line of ancient beech trees, we knew we had reached the object of our journey, Fyne Court, the mansion which was once the home of Andrew Crosse. (The place earned its name because it was once used for the collecting of manorial fines.)

The driveway sloped steeply downwards and was heavily overgrown with trees. As we drove tentatively along there was a lot of luxuriant foliage on either side of the road. We knew that the estate extended to about four hundred acres and at the end of this drive was all that remained of Fyne Court mansion.

On our left, through the drizzling rain, we could see the edge of an ornamental lake, and then beyond it a clearing amidst the trees. To one side of this was a curious little turretted construction open to the elements. It was surely Crosse's Folly, I decided — a place said at one time to have been a prison and at another a kennel for the estate dogs! I drew the car up beside it and decided to get out and investigate.

Pulling on my mackintosh, I hurried across to the Folly and went inside, out of the steadily increasing rain. Everything was still and silent as I moved cautiously about. Carefully I took a look in one of the turrets and then, despite myself, started back in horror: a colony of bats had made their home there and were sleeping away what remained of the day before commencing their nocturnal habits.

I was unable to restrain a little shudder as I walked back outside again. Next, I indicated to my wife that I was going to walk down through the trees to where I could see a group of buildings, grey and damp in the fading light.

'Crosse's Folly' — *the bat-infested building which once served as a prison.*

16

As I trudged through the damp undergrowth, I could not help feeling that both the weather and the general strangeness of the place were combining to give me a suitably eerie introduction to the locale in which Andrew Crosse lived. Time could have done little to change Fyne Court, and I almost expected to find the country mansion at the heart of the estate just as it had been when its famous owner was alive. Almost, but not quite, because I knew it had been virtually destroyed by fire in 1898.

Indeed, the little group of buildings which I found were a poor reminder of what had once been as splendid a home as any to be found in this part of Somerset. All that remained was one wing of the house, a stable block, the coach house and what my research told me had formerly been Crosse's workrooms.

Everything was absolutely still, and as I paused to look at the little complex I remembered what I had already learned about it. Built originally in the reign of Charles I about 1634, Fyne Court had belonged to members of the Crosse and Hamilton families, two lines from a single family all descended from a Norman, Odo de Sante Croce, who came to England with William the Conqueror. They had been a distinguished family, with an ancestor who lost his life at the Battle of Agincourt in 1415, and another who was a companion-at-arms to Sir Walter Raleigh on his explorations in the early 1600s. They had continued to own the house and land through Andrew Crosse's time, and even after the terrible fire in 1898 which gutted the building and made habitation impossible. In 1952, the last of the Hamiltons, Major J. A. C. Hamilton, sold the estate to a Taunton businessman, F. John C. Adams, who in 1967 bequeathed the property to the National Trust.* My reverie

* In 1974, a couple of years after my first visit, the National Trust leased Fyne Court and 22 acres of woodland to the Somerset Trust for Nature Conservancy, so that it might be turned into a conservation centre. Subsequently, the remaining buildings have been renovated — Andrew Crosse's laboratory being made into a meeting room and lecture hall, for instance — and through the hard work of the warden, David Stewart, and his helpers, the estate has been turned into a fascinating spot to visit, replete with wild life and a wide variety of flora. Sir Peter Scott, the famous ornithologist, officially declared the refurbished Fyne Court open in 1977 and it is now attracting visitors from all over the country and even abroad. The added interest of the place being Andrew Crosse's home, too, makes it well worth a visit during the hours it is open each weekend.

was finally broken when I remembered that I had heard the place was supposed to be haunted, and with the words of a poem about this flitting through my mind, I decided I had better move on before it got dark:

A sense of mystery the spirit daunted,
And said as plain as whisper in the ear —
'The place is haunted!'

To my right, as I entered what had obviously once been a courtyard, judging by the cobbles beneath my feet, there was the two-storey block which I knew had been Crosse's laboratory. Here he had conducted his experiments with electricity and crystals which had been so revolutionary in their time and made him such an object of wonder. Through the windows spotted with rain it was impossible to see anything, but if I had half hoped for some relic of the electrician to be still there, I was disappointed. I could not help feeling, though, that it was a bizarre quirk of fate that it should be the one room where Crosse had actually dabbled with the power of energy and electricity that survived the holocaust!

On my left was another small block, reached by a narrow stone staircase. This, I suspected, had once been the library which had housed a fine collection of Italian and French books collected by Andrew Crosse's father in Europe in the years prior to the French Revolution. Here, though, just visible through one of the windows, it was possible to see in the gloom the ornately plastered ceiling which looked every inch the work of Italian plasterers and must have been one of the features of the mansion during its heyday.

A coach house and stable block made up the rest of the sad remains of what I knew from an old photograph (reproduced in Chapter One) had been a magnificent building.

The rain was now falling harder still, and I sensed there was nothing further to see here. However, just as I looked up the hill towards the south east, I caught sight of something in one of the tall oak trees, now bare of its leaves for winter.

Increasing my stride, I walked across the courtyard and

18

up the slope. When I was still some way off from the tree I could see the object was a pole. Instinctively, I knew it must be one of the poles Crosse had used as lightning conductors for his work. When his experiments were at their height he had had dozens of such poles planted on their own or affixed to trees across the hillside above Fyne Court, copper wires running between them and down to his laboratory, all to catch and harness electricity from storms.

As I glanced around I could see this was probably the last remaining pole. In the falling darkness of evening, it was not hard to imagine how the whole grid of them must have frightened the local peasants on a stormy night when lightning flashed about the place and sparks leapt from the wires. To superstitious minds with no comprehension of electricity, it must have seemed that the very devils of hell were dancing around the wizard's mansion as he conducted his diabolical experiments. Today a row of telephone wires stretch down to Fyne Court forming a kind of memorial to Crosse's spider-web grid, but they are taken so much for granted as part of the scenery as to be all but invisible.

A glance at my watch now told me that if I wanted to see the church in Broomfield where Crosse was buried before night fell, I had better get back to the car right away. I was also beginning to feel rather wet, although warmed by the interest of what I was discovering.

Back in the car, as we turned around and drove up the narrow road to the village, I related to my wife what I had seen. At the gateway we turned left, went by the small common, and pulled up again outside the church we had first seen as we entered the little community.

From close up I could see that St Mary and All Saints was a dignified but austere edifice, the steady drizzle making its grey walls seem even darker. As I buttoned up my coat again in preparation for getting out, drops of rain were falling on the car from the huge tree underneath which we had pulled up beside the church gate. This was the famous thousand-year-old yew tree, said to be the third largest in all Somerset. I opened the door of the car and sprinted for the church.

St Mary's Church, Broomfield — a view from the isolated corner of the graveyard where Andrew Crosse is buried.

The oldest parts of St Mary's date from the fourteenth century, while its impressive tower was built about 1440. It is made of red sandstone, though the passage of time has turned this grey. Once inside, I was immediately impressed by the beautiful carved bench ends of the pews, on which incredibly detailed birds and sprays of foliage have been fashioned by hands that must have been still for four hundred years and more. Towering up to the roof of the building were impressive stone columns, and on the ceiling itself an array of carved wooden angels each holding a shield.

As I walked slowly around I stepped over a beautiful brass effigy, said to be the only one in the country depicting a priest in mass vestments, and then came across a massive iron-bound chest said to date from the sixteenth century. This has three locks, a key being held by the Vicar and two churchwardens so that it can only be opened when all are assembled together.

The light had almost gone completely when I found what I was looking for — a small, rather undistinguished-looking table standing on the far side opposite the south door of the church. It could have been the ordinary kind of table found in any English church, bearing a collection box or a small pile of literature. Instead, it had a band of copper stretched across it — the 'Earthing Strip' — and a notice which announced simply that it had been the bench on which Andrew Crosse had carried out his experiments. I could not restrain a smile to myself that this little wooden object, on which Crosse had worked the 'magic' which made him such a figure of fear to the local people, not to mention the clergy, should now have found its permanent resting place within the local church! I organised a photograph of the table, and then hurried back to the door to make my last visit of the day.

The rain was really heavy now, and as I turned up my collar, a distant roll of thunder echoed over the panorama of hills and fields spreading away like a brown and green-coloured quilt from the church. I went around to the north side of the church and peered into the distance. There, through the murk, I could see a stone obelisk, standing quite by itself in the corner of the churchyard.

Quickly, I picked my way over the damp grass towards the lonely stone. It seemed very eerie in the gloom, almost shunned, and I recalled that the north side of the church was always supposed to be the 'dark side' where those of uncertain character were buried. Was that what the people of Andrew Crosse's time had thought of him? And had they compelled his family to make his last resting place away from those of other decent folk of the parish? It was not a question I was ever going to be able to answer quite satisfactorily.

When I reached the obelisk I could see it was made of a light grey stone, eroded in parts and covered with patches of lichen. The inscription on it, though, was quite clear, and I read the words silently to myself:

Sacred
To the Memory of
ANDREW CROSSE
The Electrician
Born June 17th 1784
Died July 6th 1855
He was Humble Towards
God and Kind to
His Fellow Creatures

Three further lines below noted that the obelisk had been raised by Crosse's second wife, Cornelia, and that was all — no ornate figures or carved stones, no special boundary marker or details of his forebears or heirs. Andrew Crosse, as a member of one of the most distinguished of Broomfield families, lay strangely on his own in the corner of the churchyard, almost screened from view by overhanging trees and trailing weeds.

For a moment longer, I stood looking at the last resting place of the man whose story I was hoping to tell, and whose fame in literature I believed was not fully appreciated. A man who, for all his undisputed achievements and qualities, was referred to here as nothing more than 'The Electrician'. The rain continued unrelentingly down and thunder rolled again. It was all

Another relic of the 'Thunder and Lightning Man' — Andrew Crosse's table which he used for a number of his experiments and which is now kept in St Mary's Church, Broomfield.

rather like being part of a movie, considering the nature of the man and his story.

Then the scenario was completed by a flash of lightning away across the Quantock Hills. I looked up beyond the obelisk and saw the zig-zag flash down across the land. Was there not a local tradition that Crosse's tomb had been struck by lightning — a fate no other stone in the churchyard had suffered? And struck not once, but *twice*?

One final thing caught my eye as I turned away and began to squelch back over the sodden ground to the car. Along the side of the church where I was walking, a row of quite hideous, grinning gargoyles looked down onto the graves and tombstones. Such things have, of course, been placed on churches for centuries to help drive off evil spirits. I only gave them a cursory glance at first, but one which looked directly out towards Crosse's obelisk particularly caught my eye. It was perhaps more grim than the others, and in the last light of day it had a face which was vaguely familiar. I could not place it at first, and it was not until I was back in the car and we were heading once more for

Andrew Crosse's lonely tomb in St Mary's churchyard.

(Left) The gargoyle on the roof of St Mary's Church which bears such an uncanny resemblance to the face of Boris Karloff (right) as The Creature in the famous Universal Pictures version of Frankenstein *filmed in 1931.*

Bridgwater, a hot bath and a drink, that I remembered just who the gargoyle's face had reminded me of.

It was the face of Boris Karloff playing the Creature in the famous 1931 Universal film of *Frankenstein*.

3

A Boy Called 'Conjuror'

The story of Andrew Crosse is that of a young man of genius whose life and work — and the opinions they generated — turned him into a melancholy recluse in middle-age and finally an embittered old man. Few men of his generation showed more promise in the field of science and yet have suffered such neglect of their predictions and their achievements. That he should have buried himself in the isolation of his country mansion in Somerset to conduct the experiments which led the local peasantry to believe he was in league with the Devil, was perhaps not surprising, in an age still as suspicious of science as the early nineteenth century. However, the fact that the true value of his contribution to science should have been appreciated by so few is reprehensible. It is equally strange, as I shall set out to show, that his influence on a much wider field than science — that of literature — should not have been appreciated. He was a poet, to be sure, but in his early life and opinions he provided the model for a character in one of the gems of English literature: a story timeless in its appeal and as popular now as it was when written in Crosse's own day.

However, before examining this remarkable connection between an obscure Somerset scientist and the novel *Frankenstein*, I think we should know something of Crosse's life. I have assembled this from research in his home county and in Broomfield, in particular, and also from contemporary records of the man, including the now extremely rare biography of him by his second wife, Cornelia Crosse, *Memorials, Scientific and Literary, of Andrew Crosse, The Electrician*, published in 1857, two years after his death. The story of Crosse's life is an interesting and fascinating one, and at the same time, it gives us an insight into an era that was to lead to achievements in so many fields. It was an age, too, with probably more literary giants to boast than any other: Wordsworth, Coleridge, Byron, Keats, Scott, Blake, and, of course, Southey and Shelley who both happen to feature importantly in our story.

Andrew Crosse was born on June 17, 1784, the first of two sons of Richard and Susannah Crosse, at the family's ancestral home, Fyne Court. The other boy, Richard, was born in 1786. In later life, it was clear that the environment of his birth had a profound effect on the infant because he grew to love the wild and picturesque area passionately, celebrating it in his poetry, and also became very attached to his mansion home. Like those who visit the district today, he must have been exhilarated by the pure air and impressed by the view out across the Quantocks towards the Atlantic Ocean.

As I mentioned in the previous chapter, the Crosse family came from an ancient line and boasted their own coat of arms, reproduced here. These were apparently granted to Sir Richard Crosse in 1601 and he was actually knighted on the field of battle, according to the famous historian, William Camden, who was Clarenceaux king-at-arms and countersigned the document of authority.

Richard Crosse, Andrew's father, who succeeded to the family estate in 1769, was a well-educated and much-travelled man whose experience of life was far broader than many of his contemporaries. From early in his life, Crosse had shown himself to be a most accomplished scholar, fluent in the various European languages he required as he travelled all over the Continent, and an astute collector of books which made his library widely famous. He was clearly a man of character and spirit, not to mention courage, for apart from frequenting the Court of Louis XVI, he was in

Enmore Castle at the time of Andrew Crosse's birth.

The Crosse Family coat of arms granted in 1601.

28

Paris during the French Revolution and stood on the ruins of the Bastille the day it was captured. It is perhaps not surprising that his son should have become a man of determined and independent views, when we learn that the older man also held political views far from popular in England. Cornelia Crosse tells us about this in her *Memorials*:

> He [Richard] had long held liberal opinions and professed himself a republican in principle, though he had been high sheriff of Somerset only two years before these events. His views of the political changes of the day rendered him excessively unpopular; and, on one occasion when he returned from France, he was obliged to avoid the town of Bridgwater on his way home, for the populace stigmatised him with the name of Jacobin, and threatened to smash his carriage.

Despite his public opinions, Richard Crosse was a strict disciplinarian with a rigid code of honesty which he impressed on his heir from a very early age. It is said that young Andrew Crosse became so exasperated with constantly being told what an honest man his father was that he retorted on one occasion, 'Sir, would you have me the son of a rogue?'

Andrew proved himself a child with a remarkable memory, and apart from carrying a vivid picture in his mind of a family dog who died before he was two, he could recall events that occurred when he travelled with his parents through France at just four years old! For a time, the family remained at Orleans and Andrew went to school there. Then between the years of six and eight he was back in England, as a resident pupil of a Reverend White at Dorchester where he learned to read and write, remarkably mastering Greek before English!

In 1793, Andrew was sent to Dr Seyer's School in The Fort at Bristol which gained quite a reputation for the celebrated figures who were educated there, including John Kenyon, the poet and philanthropist; W. J. Broderip, the naturalist; and Reverend John Eagles, the renowned contributor to *Blackwood's Magazine*. All of these schoolfellows we shall hear of again in our story.

Although he was a small, thin, wiry boy, young Andrew

was well able to look after himself when taunted by older boys, and delighted in pranks and mischief which made him popular with the other pupils but earned him frequent canings from his masters. In quieter moments he read voraciously and 'delighted in whatever was strange and marvellous', according to Cornelia Crosse.

The youngster's imagination was clearly developing, and in the holidays he and his brother, Richard, would create a whole fantasy world complete with its own language and creatures rather like large fir cones whom they called 'hoblegees'. The boys used to imagine themselves being pursued by these creatures as they scurried through the passages of Fyne Court. They also invented peculiar laws and institutions for their fantasy land, and the ideas apparently persisted in their minds for several years until approaching maturity turned Richard, in particular, to other pursuits.

Two of the major complaints that Andrew and his fellow pupils nursed about their school were the meagre meals they were allowed and the very short holidays they were given. In a report found among his papers and quoted by his wife, Crosse recalls how they tried to resolve this situation:

On one occasion we got up a rebellion; we resolved to stand out for longer holidays. We arranged to barricade the schoolroom; we provided ourselves with muskets, and we had settled among ourselves what boys should station themselves at the windows, and when they were shot down which others should take their place. We were desperately earnest; not a boy but what was prepared to die at his post. However, the plot was discovered before it was ripe for execution; the muskets were seized, the ringleaders expelled, others flogged; how I escaped I know not. One of these lads was afterwards midshipman in Nelson's squadron, and was cut down while bravely boarding an enemy's ship. But the most singular part of the business was that some of the Irish newspapers magnified our intended barring-out into an act of political disaffection, and reported in their columns that the government was so unpopular that the British school boys were prepared to head a formidable riot of the townspeople. So much for the truth of history.

If such a narrow escape might be expected to calm down young Andrew, that was not what happened. Indeed, he ran full pelt into the very thing that was to influence the rest of his life: science.

The teaching of science in schools such as that of Dr Seyer was fairly rudimentary, and it is unlikely that it took much of Andrew's attention until his class began to discuss the making of fireworks. This clearly fascinated him, as we can see when he relates another prank which his sense of mischief lead him into.

I was always very fond of making fireworks. One day, while learning my Virgil, I continued to carry on the business of pounding some rocket mixture; but, as ill luck would have it, Seyer discovered my twofold employment, and immediately took away the mixture from me in considerable wrath. I watched where he put it; it was on the window-sill of a room which was always kept locked; the window, though not glazed, had close iron bars through which nothing could pass; the case was hopeless; I could not recover my rocket mixture, but a happy thought struck me, I was resolved that no one else should enjoy the spoil which I regarded as so valuable. I had a burning glass in my pocket, and I thought of Archimedes and the Roman fleet; the sun was shining, and I soon drew a focus on the gunpowder, which immediately blew up. It was well that the house was not set on fire: as for me, I was reckless of all consequences.

Andrew's interest in science really began to grow when he was 12 years old and he started to learn about electricity. The subject was one that he might well have heard a little about at home, for his father was a friend of two of the pioneers of electricity, Benjamin Franklin (1706–90), who explained fully the difference between positive and negative electricity and devised the lightning conductor, and Joseph Priestley (1733–1804), the clergyman and chemist who wrote the famous work, *History of Electricity*, in 1767. Mrs Crosse remarks on this important aspect of her future husband's life:

Mr Crosse's father had been a friend of Franklin and Priestley;

31

so we may conclude that he had some scientific tastes: but I never heard that he had directed his son's attention to these subjects. He may, perhaps, almost unconsciously have become interested in electricity or chemistry from hearing his father's personal recollections of these two distinguished philosophers.

Many years later, when deeply buried in his experiments, Andrew Crosse light-heartedly attributed his attraction to science as having been caused by an empty stomach! For he had made a habit, whenever he had enough money, of going to a tavern not far from the school to supplement his meagre diet with a plate of boiled beef. 'Never shall I forget,' he said, 'those lunches the good old soul at the tavern used to cut off for me: she generally gave me more than my money's worth; for she knew I was a schoolboy and felt a pity for me. One day while discussing my beef, my eye fell upon a bill containing the syllabus of a course of lectures on Natural Science: the first of the series was on optics. I conceived a great wish to hear the lecturer; I asked and obtained permission of Mr Seyer, to subscribe to the course. The second course was on electricity; my future tastes were decided.'

Whether this story is true or apocryphal, there is no doubt that once Andrew Crosse had discovered the world of electricity, his whole life was changed. Every other subject at school took second place to this new obsession, and though he continued to be an above average pupil in most subjects, it was the mysteries of electrical currents that absorbed his waking hours.

In 1800, when he was just 16, Andrew Crosse's father died suddenly, and he came into the sole care of his mother who soon proved an indulgent parent prepared to forgive the excesses which his late parent would certainly have condoned and punished. Reports that he was wasting time at school with pranks or spending too much time in experimentation, were dismissed by her as just examples of his youthful high spirits.

There was no denying, though, that Crosse's love of electrical science was growing all the time. In fact, there is still in existence a copy of a letter to Mrs Cornelia Crosse from one of her husband's contemporaries at school, describing an early experiment he carried out. The man, John Jenkyns, writes:

> I dare say he has mentioned to you our first joint attempt in the science of electricity, and the wonderment occasioned to a circle of school boys by giving them a shock with a Leyden phial (a bottle which was sent to one of us with a dose of physic from the apothecary), charged by a broken glass or a barometer; the bottle was coated by myself, and I think he has told me not long since, that it was still in his possession. I fear that my knowledge did not go much further, but the world knows well what progress was made by my fellow-workman.

Another first former at the school at this time — Crosse was then in the sixth form — was W. J. Broderip, who was later to gain fame as a naturalist. He has left us a graphic description of how he came into painful contact with one of Crosse's electrical pranks. (By way of explanation, it should be mentioned that all first form pupils at the school were known as 'Blacks' and were much bullied by the older boys.)

> I well remember being brought up by a fifth-former named Woodford to what I took for an old witch who was standing by an upright sort of doorless box; one of the 'presses', as they were called, which stood in the hall. At the back of the box was a transparency representing a place which is said to be paved with good intentions; and before it, suspended and apparently dancing, pitchfork in hand, a frightful medieval devil. While I gazed in horror, a shock shot through my terrified frame, which I must have borne tolerably well, for I was afterward let into the secret, and assisted in bringing up other 'Blacks' to the scratch.
>
> The first electrifying machine was a broken barometer tube, rubbed with amalgam spread upon a piece of leather, which, if I recollect right, formed part of the lining of Ben Watkin's pumps. The Leyden vial was an apothecary's bottle, coated by John Jenkyns. The old witch was Andrew in a great coat with a pocket handkerchief tied under his chin and covering his head, and Jenkyns was in attendance as a kind of familiar enjoying the terror and astonishment of the 'Black.'

Mr Broderip says that he later learned that the Devil was

suspended by a single human hair which was quite invisible to the human eye and therefore made the figure all the more terrifying to the young viewer. By way of contrast, he remembers Crosse as having been a generous soul as well as a prankster, and a tough fighter when challenged. On one occasion, after a particularly bruising contest with another sixth-former, he was exhibited, black-eyed and swollen-nosed, in front of the whole school by Dr Seyer as a warning to others.

Such devices as the medieval Devil soon earned him the nickname 'Conjuror' Crosse, and so keen was his enthusiasm for experimentation that he began saving his money not for plates of beef at the Bristol tavern, but rather for new pieces of electrical equipment. What he could not afford to buy, he wrote home about in begging letters to his mother asking for the money. She did not refuse him.

The shop in Bristol where he went to purchase the equipment also provided him with another important encounter in his life. Among the books on electricity which he had been reading, one described some experiments carried out by a man named Nicholls which had particularly stuck in his mind. He wrote later:

When purchasing my equipment, I entered into a philosophical discussion with the old man who kept the shop. I told him I was very curious about some experiments performed by a namesake of his mentioned in *Nicholson's Dictionary*. 'Oh!' said he, 'I am the person. Those experiments you speak of are mine.' 'What!' I exclaimed in perfect amazement, 'are you really the person mentioned in the book? How glad I am to talk with you'. I cannot describe the profound respect I felt for the old man, and with what intense interest I listened to all he said. That I should know a real electrician, a man whose name was printed in a book with other philosophers, seemed to me an epoch in my life.

Crosse's last year at the Bristol school seems to have been one long round of experiments, either under the supervision of masters as part of the science classes — where he far outstripped his fellow pupils in terms of ability — or else surreptitiously during the breaks from lessons. His schemes for giving younger pupils electric shocks grew more ambitious as they came to suspect his every motive, and he baffled a number of masters as to why they were suddenly mildly electrocuted by touching some previously harmless object like a handle of a doorknob which 'Conjuror' Crosse had cunningly wired up to his 'electrifying machine'.

In June 1802 the time arrived for Andrew to leave Dr Seyer's school and go on to Oxford, where he entered Brazenose College. Here, though, he was suddenly no longer the mischievous idol of the school, but a freshman prey to all the temptations which were University life in the early years of the nineteenth century.

The city of Oxford was, of course, nothing like the size it is today, and its University consisted of twenty colleges and five 'halls' with a total membership including professors and students of just two thousand. It was a hotbed of extremist viewpoints and indulgence of students and staff, to the extent that few lectures were actually given and even those were poorly attended. Contemporary reports indicate that the tutors were morose, insipid and profligate, and the examinations which were held were so arranged that the students had every opportunity to memorise the questions beforehand and very few indeed failed to pass. By general consent a degree was given not for ability but length of residence.

Naturally enough discipline was extremely lax, and this allowed the students virtually unlimited freedom to indulge themselves in drinking, gambling and even immorality. In fact, amusing oneself rather than studying was the order of the day with most students, and they wasted no time in drawing new undergraduates into the same ways.

Crosse had come to Oxford ostensibly to continue his study of Greek, Latin, logic and divinity — the standard course — and though he suspected the life might prove congenial to someone of his temperament, he realised it would not allow him to continue his study of science, and electricity in particular. In fact, as Cornelia Crosse notes in her biography, Andrew found Oxford 'a sad place of temptation for a young and inexperienced boy'.

35

Crosse himself expanded on this later in life. 'I always hated wine,' he said, 'but I had not the moral courage to refuse joining the parties which were made up by my companions. What chance is there for an unfortunate lad just come from school — launched into every species of extravagance — no one to watch or care for him – no guide? (I often saw my tutor carried off perfectly intoxicated.) Most likely he falls in with ill-advisers — and no one feels any shame, but the false shame of doing right.'

Even as he succumbed to temptation, though, Andrew Crosse tried to retain some of the qualities his father had endeavoured to instil in him. A revealing statement quoted by Cornelia Crosse showed what a struggle this must have been. Said Crosse, 'I remember once we were reading Aristotle on Friendship — "Don't you think this rather too romantic?" observed my tutor. "Not at all, sir," I replied: "I think a man ought to make every sacrifice for his friend." I saw a smile of derision pass round the room, and I said no more. I felt I was not understood. Ridicule is a terrible trial to the young, and nothing is more rare than moral courage.'

It is hardly surprising that under these circumstances, Andrew should have described the University in a letter to his mother as 'a perfect hell upon earth'. There was no doubt he looked forward eagerly to the end of term when he could slip back to the peace and tranquillity of Broomfield and Fyne Court.

The years between 1802 and 1805 continued in this desultory fashion for Crosse, and what little work he did in the field of electricity was confined to brief experiments while he was on holiday. Then in 1805 tragedy struck his life — in July his mother died, just a month to the day after he had passed his 21st birthday. He was heart-broken, and the element of melancholy which was to so dominate his character revealed itself for the first time.

Andrew had loved his mother dearly, and even if her counsel had often been too liberal, he did miss having an adult to turn to for guidance of some kind. Now, of course, he inherited the family home and estate, although he had little business sense to guide him. So, he allowed others to run the place for him and seemingly trusted people quite indiscriminately. As Mrs Crosse has written, 'He soon became a dupe to the dishonesty of some, and a victim of his own and others' mismanagement.'

Andrew's brother, Richard, was also living with him at Fyne Court, as was a step-sister from his father's first marriage. Their group soon became well known for their lavish hospitality at home, and the parties that they threw for an ever-increasing circle of 'acquaintances' in both Somerset and London. To a degree, this company lifted Andrew Crosse out of the mood of melancholy brought on by his mother's death, and there are indications he began to start playing jokes again with electrical machines. In a world such as the one in which he lived, he was clearly wondering if there was any point in worrying about tomorrow. He might just as well spend his inheritance and let the future take care of itself.

Just when it seemed Crosse might become yet another young society waster who would squander his fortune until destitution stared him in the face, he met the man who was to rekindle his interest in science and encourage him to continue his electrical experiments, George John Singer. The two were introduced at a dinner party in London and, once they had exhausted the idle gossip so common at such gatherings, they discovered they shared a mutual interest.

Singer, who was born in 1786, came from a humble background, his mother running an artificial flower-making business in Prince's Street, off Cavendish Square in London. His early years were hard ones, and after his brief period at school he reluctantly entered the family business — reluctantly, because he had already become fascinated with electrical experimentation.

In whatever spare time he could find from the business of making flowers, he built himself a laboratory at the back of his home, and there indulged his real interest. He was forced because of his circumstances to make most of his own equipment, and he also supplemented his meagre funds by giving demonstrations and lectures to anyone who would come and listen. By his own admission, these public performances were sprinkled with explosions and electrical displays to catch the imagination of the impressionable. However, it brought in the money to allow him to develop his work — and it also enabled him to invent a number of items, including a gold-leaf electrometer. He was also working on a book which, when it was published, was to prove an important contribution to electrical science.

The friendship between the two young contemporaries flourished immediately. Mrs Crosse tells us they were frequent companions:

> Mr Singer supplied him with his splendid cylindrical electrical machine and battery table, which contained fifty large Leyden jars. The friends spent many pleasant days at Broomfield, in working together at statical electricity. They also used to take long walks over the Quantock hills ... Mr Crosse used long after to point out to me the paths they had taken over the hills, and he would recall their conversations together with great satisfaction, the more so, I suspect, because his opportunities of intellectual intercourse were few and far between.

Thoroughly stimulated, Andrew Crosse now spent less time in entertaining and more in work. He busied himself becoming a good practical chemist, began the study of mineralogy, and planned a series of electrical experiments. At this time, his experiments were primarily directed towards testing his electrical machine under varying conditions and defining the equality of the charging power of the positive and negative conductors. To all his work he brought an open mind: one prepared to look at the possibilities from every angle, even if this meant contradicting already well-established principles. If progress was to be made in the field of electricity, he reasoned, it had to be made with original thought and painstaking labour. Mrs Crosse has commented on this trait in his nature:

> This peculiarity of clearing for himself a path in pursuit of an idea induced great originality both in the manner in which he conducted his researches and in the discoveries which ensued. He never accepted anything as true without first proving it by experiment, unless, indeed, the rationale of the proposition was such that it could not be otherwise. But if he viewed the cause of

the phenomena as arising from certain *unacknowledged* laws, he would not abandon his position, or desist from inquiry, because all former experience and the received explanation were opposed to the results which followed his experiments.

In 1807, encouraged by his friend George Singer, Crosse began a series of experiments into electro-crystallisation. What prompted this work was the discovery by some labourers, a few years earlier, of an aperture in the rock of a limestone quarry in Broomfield. This they widened to reveal an extensive fissure. The roof and sides of the place were covered with white agonite crystals, and shortly afterwards it was named Holwell Cavern.*

This amazing and colourful array of crystals naturally attracted many visitors, including Andrew Crosse, who initially found himself inspired to write a poem about the place. The opening verse ran:

> Now pierce the hill's steep side, where dark as night
> Holwell's rude cavern claims the torch's light;
> Where, breathless, dank, the fissure cleaves in twain
> The unchiselled rock which threats to close again,
> And swallow in its adamantine jaws
> The bold explorer of creation's laws.

However, after a number of visits to Holwell, Crosse found that the stalactites and stalagmites were beginning to interest the scientific side of his nature as well as the poetic. The more he pondered on the laws which governed the growth of crystals, the more difficult he found it to believe that the starry emanations from the centres were the effect of mere mechanical dropping of water charged with carbonate of lime. So he resolved to experiment, and later reported in a note which has survived:

---

* Interestingly, it has been suggested that Sir Arthur Conan Doyle used this cavern as the hiding place for the Quantock smugglers in his novel, *Micah Clarke*. Certainly, Sir Arthur spent some time in the area absorbing local colour before writing his story of the Monmouth Rebellion, and as Holwell is the only natural cave in West Somerset, the likelihood he had the place in mind seems very strong. He further described the place as being hung with long lime crystals that sparkled and gleamed in the light of torches. Holwell Cavern still exists today, but has been closed to the public for some years because of the wholesale removal of the crystals by previous visitors.

Each time I visited this cavern, I felt assured that I should sooner or later learn some new principle from an examination of its interesting crystallisation. I felt convinced at an early period that the formation and constant growth of the crystalline matter which lined the roof of this cave was caused by some peculiar upward attraction; and, reasoning more on the subject, I felt assured that it was electric attraction. I brought away some water from Holwell Cave, and filling a tumbler with it exposed it to the action of a small voltaic battery excited by water alone. The opposite poles of the battery were connected with the Holwell water by platinum wires, let fall at opposite sides of the tumbler. An electric action immediately took place, which continued for nine days; but not finding any formation upon either of the wires, I was about to take abroad the whole apparatus, when at that precise moment a party of friends called, and remained some time. This most fortunate delay prevented the removal of the apparatus till the next or tenth day, when I went for the purpose of so doing; the sun was shining brightly, and I plainly observed some sparkling crystals upon the negative platinum wire, which proved to be carbonate of lime, attracted from the mineral waters by the electric action.

To be quite sure of his discovery, Crosse repeated the experiment in pitch darkness to reproduce exactly the conditions in which the crystals had grown in the cave. Again another batch of sparkling crystals formed, this time by the sixth day.

Absorbed though he was in this work, Crosse must have found time for social pursuits, because in 1809 he got married. His wife was Mary Anne Hamilton, the daughter of a distinguished local Army Captain. Cornelia, his second wife, admits in her book that there are scant records of this lady, and we know little more of her except that during the next ten years, she bore Andrew seven children, three of whom died in childhood. She also seems to have mostly suffered very poor health. Although it is evident Andrew was very fond of his wife, the deaths of his children continued to play on his already morbid inclinations, as did the increasing problems thrown up in the management of the Fyne Court estate. Never a practical man at the best of times, he most wanted to be left alone to his experiments, but did try his best for his wife and family. Remorselessly, it seemed, a shadow was already beginning to spread over his life which would only grow bigger with the passage of time.

In the next five years, Andrew Crosse directed much of his time in Broomfield to scientific work, following increasingly along a new line of research concerning electricity and the elements. He set up his network of copper wires strung on poles across Fyne Court, all connected with his laboratory — or 'electrical room' as he sometimes called it — and with this he began a lengthy series of tests to establish the amounts and nature of the electricity in the atmosphere. As we shall learn later, it was demanding work which proved surprising, not to mention dangerous, at times!

During this period, Crosse made very few visits to London, and then almost solely at the instigation of his friend, George Singer, so that they might discuss the progress they were making in their respective ways. Singer, though, was now publishing details of his work quite regularly, and had become a contributor to the *Philosophical Magazine*. He was also giving an increasing number of lectures and had virtually completed work on his *magnum opus*. He urged Crosse to make public something of his own experiments with electrical forces, but when the Somersetshire man would not, implored him at least to come up to London and give a lecture to interested parties. Singer said that he was particularly anxious Crosse should meet a man named Michael Faraday, then assistant to the great Humphrey Davy, who attended his lectures and was apparently making giant strides in research into the problems of electricity. There were also other members of the London scientific and social circles who would be most interested in hearing about his work.

The first sign that Crosse was weakening in his resolve was when he agreed to allow Singer to publish some details of his research in the book he was completing. This was entitled *Elements of Electricity and Electro-Chemistry*, and when it appeared in November 1814 it was greeted with the kind of widespread and resounding praise not usually lavished on such scientific works. In a very short space of time it was being authoritatively considered as the most important work of its kind, and translations were being prepared into all the major European languages. When Singer again pressed Crosse to come to London and discuss his work, now that some details were known, he was unable to refuse.

So, in December, after a quiet Christmas Day with his family in Somerset, Andrew Crosse made the two-day journey up to London. He found it buzzing with talk of electrics and electricians as a result of the success of Singer's book. He told his friend he *would* lecture on his work — but on one condition. He would not speak in Singer's own lecture hall. True to the sense of honesty that had never deserted him, he did not want it thought he was being given a platform to air his opinions under his friend's patronage. Singer, for his part, was quite content with this condition, and had no trouble whatsoever in securing Crosse the opportunity to lecture at another well-known gathering place for scientific talks, Garnerin's. The only problem was that Crosse would have to speak that self-same night! Fortunately he had already made some notes, and rather than wait around anxiously for another opportunity, he decided to plunge right in, forget the weariness he felt from his journey, and give his talk there and then.

And so it was on the night of Wednesday, December 28, that Andrew Crosse, the retiring electrician from the heart of the Quantock Hills, stood up to face his audience in Garnerin's. It was a packed audience for so soon after the Christmas festivities, but an attentive and interested one for all that. It consisted of the usual cross-section of prosperous and intelligent London citizens drawn from the worlds of science, commerce and even literature. Probably it would have deserved no more than a footnote in any history book, except for the fact that two young people were in the audience who were later to shake the world, both because of their life-style and their genius. And one of whom was to use elements of the man who addressed them in creating an enduring literary masterpiece.

They were the promising young poet and radical, Percy Bysshe Shelley, and his beautiful, teenage mistress, Mary Wollstonecraft Godwin.

42

4

An Electric Romance!

The love story of the poet Shelley and the beautiful young Mary Wollstonecroft Godwin is as famous as any in history, and in its ingredients of a tortured man of genius, married, but none the less falling for a teenage girl, there is the very stuff of great romance. It is a story that has often been told, both in biographies of these two remarkable people and in studies of nineteenth century literature in which they both play such an important part. Perhaps here it would be useful to briefly sketch in a few details of their respective lives, how they came together, and the influences which caused them to play a part in our story. I shall begin with the young man, Shelley.

Percy Bysshe Shelley was born on August 4, 1792, at Field Place, near Horsham in Sussex. His father, Timothy Shelley, was a wealthy country squire and Member of Parliament. The boy's background was conservative enough, to be sure, but from his infancy young Percy revealed an outspoken and imaginative mind which went far beyond the boundaries of such a society. His childhood was evidently happy, and perhaps remarkable for the fact that he early developed a skill for storytelling and would keep his four adoring sisters entranced for hours with stories of witches and monsters, which apparently frightened both them and him!

At the age of ten, in 1802, he entered Sion House Academy at Isleworth near Brentford, and there first demonstrated the restlessness and rebellious nature which were to characterise so much of his life. Accustoming himself to this way of life was not helped by the fact that he was a slightly-built, rather girlish-looking lad who had no interest in sport or the other usual pursuits of boys. However, what he lacked in stature he made up for in imagination, as Sir John Rennie has noted in his *Autobiography* (1875): 'His imagination was always roving upon something romantic and extraordinary such as spirits, fairies, lightning, volcanoes, etc, and he not infrequently astonished his schoolfellows by blowing up the boundary palings of the playground with gunpowder, also the lid of his desk in the middle of schooltime, to the great surprise of Dr Greenlaw and the whole school. In fact, at times he was considered to be almost on the borders of insanity.' (If the reader is aware of a strange similarity between Shelley's early years and those of Andrew Crosse, it is heightened all the more by Shelley's comment that he considered his schooldays 'a perfect hell'.)

At Sion House, Shelley also began surreptitiously to read cheap 'Blue books' of horrid stories and multivolumed Gothic novels obtained from a seedy lending library in Brentford. These not only gave him nightmares but also sowed the seeds of his first 'grim' poems. Indeed, this literature of terror and wonder was to have a profound effect on his mind which time never eradicated. What may have excited him even more, perhaps, were the scientific demonstrations which were given occasionally to the pupils by one Adam Walker, a self-taught natural philosopher and inventor of scientific toys. As Newman I. White in his biography, *Shelley* (1947), has written, 'Various experiments at Field Place, Sion House Academy and later Eton with gunpowder and fire may have originated from other sources, non-scientific in nature; but it is very probable that Adam Walker was the starting point for the electrical experiments, burning-glasses, microscopes, Leyden jars, and chemical mixtures that Shelley toyed with for about ten years thereafter.'

The brilliant young poet and radical, Percy Bysshe Shelley.

These lessons opened up a whole new world for Shelley, and during his holidays at Field Place there are tales of his dressing up as a devil and setting off explosions and laying electric shocks to frighten his family and relatives. (Shades of Andrew Crosse again!) White tells us: 'There were also chemical and electrical experiments with shocks, and electrical cures for chilblains which Hellen (his sister) dreaded and was finally excused from participating in. Like Franklin, he flew kites to catch electricity. When he left home to enter Eton, the washroom reeked with smoke from some experiment gone awry.'

Shelley entered Eton in July 1804. The life at Sion House

and the development of his imagination and attitudes had already made him something of a rebel, but once more his rather effeminate appearance made him the target of bullying and abuse. When he again got a reputation for being an odd-man-out, he was nick-named 'Mad Shelley'. There is, however, a story that he actually led a revolt against the infamous 'fagging' system which allowed the older boys to force the young pupils to do all their chores for them, but no evidence has come to light to support this claim.

Science and chemistry were not a part of the curriculum at Eton, so Shelley only had the chance to follow his interests rather furtively. The risk of punishment he ran was all the greater because, a few months after he had entered the college, a boy had been killed when some fireworks were accidentally exploded. None the less, he continued to experiment with chemical 'brews' and indeed very nearly blew himself up on one occasion! Electricity particularly fascinated him, and after electrifying a tom cat — Newman White tells us — 'he even electrified "Butch" Bethell when that blundering tutor and landlord too hastily investigated a galvanic battery'. His interest also took him into the by-ways of science: to the ancient books of chemistry and magic by Albertus Magnus and Paracelsus, as well as all the pseudo-science and incantations associated with the supernatural. According to more than one biographer, he actually tried to raise a ghost and spent a night among the bones of the dead in a charnel house!

Aside from these sensation-seeking diversions, he was always attempting to push forward his knowledge of science and found his greatest inspiration in the work of Franklin, whom he 'swore by'. He was starting to write, too, and after failing to complete one novel entitled *The Nightmare*, he finished a second, *Zastrozzi*, a tale of Gothic passions, which was published in 1810. Shelley's name did not appear on the work, and although it was roundly condemned by one critic as being the work of 'a diseased brain' and full of 'gross and wanton pages', Shelley was pleased to have been published and even enjoyed his infamy. Infamy, indeed, was a quality he was to become increasingly acquainted with throughout his life.

In 1810 Shelley was sent by his father to Oxford University, and he probably nursed hopes that his life might be a little better there than it had been at Eton. The place had not changed in the slightest since Andrew Crosse had passed through Brazenose College. Shelley found his fellow scholars more given to discussion than bullying, more inclined to laziness than fighting, and he was soon launching into eulogies about science and chemistry. Newman White has written of this period of the young poet's life:

> Shelley proved himself a true disciple of Adam Walker in a glowing account of the blessings humanity would shortly inherit from sciences as yet only in their infancy. Synthetic foods and fertilizers, the discovery of new principles of heating and irrigation, the control of electricity, would render human life infinitely less toilsome and uncomfortable. Man had only just learned to lift himself from the earth in balloons, but eventually unexplored regions would be charted from the air. It is a remarkable fact that ... these speculations have practically all been verified.

Contemporary reports indicate that Shelley packed his room in University College with scientific and electrical equipment, and frequently gave demonstrations with his electrical machine and his galvanic battery. The furniture and floors were stained with the results of experiments that had gone wrong (no change from those at home, it seems!), and the air was often foul with strange odours. His friends began to regard him as something of a wizard, and if anyone had been asked to predict his future they would surely have said it lay in the fields of science.

Shelley was clearly happy at Oxford and he had plenty of time to indulge his other passions for reading and writing. This was to lead him to the book which was to prove the most important single work he read at Oxford — indeed at any time — William Godwin's *An Enquiry into Political Justice*, published in 1793. It is possible he heard about the work while he was at Eton, but it was at Oxford that he definitely secured his own copy. This book of revolutionary ideas about government and morality was to have a profound effect on his future thought and action. As we have seen, whenever anything interested Shelley — as chemistry and electricity had done — he devoted himself passionately to it. Furthermore, Godwin's ideas on political and social reform seemed to provide the perfect intellectual justification for his growing hatred of authority. From the moment he discovered *Political Justice*, he had found a new God to replace that of science in his affections. As he told a friend, Godwin was now 'the regulator and former of my mind'.

What he could not have known, of course, was that Godwin was to figure in his life as more than just the author of a seminal book. He was also the father of a young girl named Mary whose life was shortly to become inextricably entwined with his own.

Excited by all the thoughts of radicalism running through his head, Shelley now concocted a work of his own which threatened a bigger explosion than any of his experiments. It was a short pamphlet entitled *The Necessity of Atheism*, in which he explained his reasons for disbelief in the existence of God. It raised an immediate storm of protest in Oxford when it was published in March 1811 — copies were actually seized and burned — and Shelley was summarily expelled from the college. He felt shocked and bewildered, and was quite unable to understand how anyone was unable or unwilling to listen to the irrefutable logic of his arguments.

In hindsight, Shelley's expulsion was a disaster to a young man of such a restless and unstable nature. At 19 years of age he was thrown out on to the world, and his indulgent father now felt resentful and distrustful of him. There was no way the boy could follow him into politics and his lack of business sense seemed to completely rule out the possibility of him managing the family estate at Field Place. Almost against his better judgement, he settled an allowance on his son until he came of age.

There was only one place for Shelley to go and that was London, so there he took himself and determined to try and make a living from his pen. For a while, his one solace were the visits which a school friend of his sister, a pretty blonde girl named Harriet Westbrook, began to pay to his lodgings in Poland Street. In a matter of weeks, the impetuous

Shelley believed he was in love, and imagining Harriet to be as oppressed as himself, eloped with her to Edinburgh where they were married without parental consent in August 1811. On their return journey to London, the now ostracised couple stopped for a while at Keswick in the Lake District. There, with some trepidation, Percy introduced himself to Robert Southey, the poet and free-thinker whose works he had first discovered and admired while at Oxford. The two radicals were to meet again in London, and Southey is to play a significant part in our story.

Back once more in the capital, Percy Shelley suddenly recalled the man who had opened his mind to new avenues of thought, William Godwin, and determined to make his acquaintance. He wrote to the philosopher as an ardent admirer of his work and was almost immediately welcomed into his fold. It has been suggested that the cold and remote Godwin was welcoming because he believed Shelley to be the heir to a large fortune, while he himself was, as always, in financial difficulties: but this has never been substantiated.

For a time, contact between the two was carried on mainly through correspondence, as the restless Shelley travelled in both Ireland and Wales writing and expounding his proposals for reform. It was not until he and Harriet were back in London in the winter of 1812 that they began to enjoy personal contact with Godwin and his family. When this happened, the die of Shelley's fate was cast.

William Godwin was born in 1756 in Wisbech and after being educated at a Presbyterian College entered the ministry. However, during a cathartic five year period in East Anglia, he turned from a believer into an atheist and, more particularly, a radical. The French Revolution seemed to stir his imagination and the result in 1793 was *Political Justice*, the book which made him famous. The work was calmly subversive of everything, particularly the law and marriage, but it did deprecate violence, which may have been the one feature which prevented the outraged authorities from prosecuting him. He further substantiated his fame with a novel, *The Adventures of Caleb Williams* (1794), which gave a 'General review of the modes of·domestic and unrecorded despotism', to quote the author. It was shortly after this that Mary Wollstonecraft came into his life; the woman who, to everyone's surprise, he married.

Mary Wollstonecraft, who is today regarded as perhaps the first great feminist, was born in 1759 in London, and showed a determined streak in her nature when still a teenager by leaving home to make her own living. For a time she worked in publishing and her acquaintanceship with a number of literary figures encouraged her to write her first book, *Vindication of the Rights of Man* (1790), as an answer to Edmund Burke's *Reflections on the French Revolution*, published earlier that same year. Two years later she produced *Vindication of the Rights of Woman*, which advocated equality of the sexes and outlined the main doctrines of the later women's movement. The book gained her instant notoriety. Shortly after this, she was involved in an unhappy affair with an American, Captain Gilbert Imlay, who fathered a daughter by her and then deserted her. In her despair she tried to commit suicide by jumping in the Thames, but when this failed she decided to cast her lot in with William Godwin; she had met him briefly in 1791 and he seemed to share her republican sympathies. It was when Mary was four months pregnant with Godwin's child that these two renowned radicals amazed their circle of friends by getting married in March 1797. The infant, named Mary Wollstonecraft Godwin, was born after a difficult period of labour in the August; by the following month, the ill-fated mother was dead.

It is perhaps not surprising that with two such remarkable parents, young Mary should prove a strong-willed, imaginative and ultimately influential person, and equally that she should be destined for a life filled with passion and tragedy. For three years she and her step-sister, Fanny Imlay, were reared almost solely by a housekeeper and then, in 1801, their father married again. His new bride was Mary Jane Clairmont, who already had two children of her own, a boy, Charles, and a girl, Clara. Fanny appears to have taken well to her new mother, but Mary obviously disliked her intensely and was soon displaying the rebellious

The beautiful young author of Frankenstein, *Mary Wollstonecraft Shelley.*

tendencies which shaped her life. Competition between the two sets of children was increased all the more when a son, William, was born to Godwin and his new wife in 1803.

Deprived of her real mother's love and with her father so often absorbed in his literary work and his financial problems, Mary retreated into a world of books, daydreams and fantasies. She also began her first hesitant attempts at writing. Her education was as haphazard as that of the other children, for Godwin did not believe in regimented learning and they were left very much to their own devices. However, the occasions when her father's literary and radical friends called at their home brought Mary out of her shell, for she had the opportunity of listening-in to their conversations. Such talk can only have further influenced her wilful nature.

In 1811, Mrs Godwin prevailed on her husband that it would be in Mary's best interests for her to be sent away for some formal education. So the 14-year-old was packed off to a boarding school in Ramsgate which, if anything, further heightened her sense of being an isolated and solitary soul, for she had little in common with the other girls. It seems, too, that she was away in Scotland with family friends when the young man who was to play such an important role in her life began calling on her father.

The first real contact between Percy Bysshe Shelley and Mary Godwin did not occur until the spring of 1814, a year that was to prove a tumultuous one for both of them. Mary was now sixteen and a half and something of a beauty. Shelley had reached his maturity and had also just published *Queen Mab*, the first of his important poems. On the one side was a young woman searching for a seemingly illusive object on which to focus her dormant love; on the other an idealistic and radical young poet rapidly beginning to regret his hasty marriage.

Irresistibly, the two young people were drawn together as Shelley called daily at the Godwin household, ostensibly to converse with the philosopher, but increasingly for a meeting with Mary. In a later letter written to a friend, Shelley graphically described what was happening to him that spring:

> I speedily conceived an ardent passion to possess this inestimable treasure. In my own mind this feeling assumed a variety of shapes. I disguised from myself the true nature of my affection. I endeavoured also to conceal it from Mary, but without success. I was vacillating and infirm of purpose: I shuddered to transgress a real duty, and could not in this instance perceive the boundaries by which virtue was separated from madness, where self-devotion becomes the very

52

prodigality of idiotism. No expressions can convey the remotest conception of the manner in which she dispelled my delusions. The sublime and rapturous moment when she confessed herself mine, who had so long been hers in secret, cannot be painted to mortal imaginations.

The declaration of their love for each other inspired Shelley to write a poem to Mary which he dated June, 1814. One verse, in particular, summed up the position they now found themselves in:

> We are not happy, sweet! our state
> Is strange and full of doubt and fear;
> More need of words that ills abate; —
> Reserve or censure come not near
> Our sacred friendship, lest there be
> No solace left for you and me.

As William Godwin had declared himself to be a believer in free love, it might have seemed likely that he would have no objection to the love between his admirer and his daughter. He might even have found it all the harder to protest at their association because Shelley had just arranged to loan him some money to help him out of his latest financial crisis. But object he certainly did, as he revealed in a letter to a friend in August, 1814:

On Sunday, June 26, he [Shelley] accompanied Mary and her sister to the tomb of Mary's mother, one mile distant from London; and there, it seems, an impious idea first occurred to him of seducing her, playing the traitor to me, and deserting his wife. On Wednesday, the 6th of July, the transaction of the loan was completed; and on the evening of that very day he had the madness to disclose his plans to me, and to ask my consent. I expostulated with him with all the energy of which I was master, and with so much effect that for the moment he promised me to give up his licentious love and return to virtue. I applied all my diligence to waken up a sense of honour and natural affection in the mind of Mary, and I seemed to have succeeded. They both deceived me.

In an attempt to end the affair, Godwin banned Shelley

from his home and forbade Mary to think of the young poet again. However, their passionate natures were not to be so easily diverted. Shelley took the remarkable step of informing his ill-used wife, Harriet, that he had fallen in love with Mary Godwin and suggested that they should all live together. The stunned young woman who had herself been, as she imagined, rescued from a dominant father by the young poet, had not the will to do anything other than agree. She also probably hoped the infatuation with Mary would cease after a while.

For a short time, Shelley overcame the worst frustrations of the enforced separation by secretly arranging for notes to be delivered to Mary. Then one morning his passion became stronger than his pen and he rushed into Godwin's house and confronted Mary. Wildly excited, he suggested they commit suicide so that 'Death shall unite us', but before anything further could happen, Mrs Godwin appeared and persuaded the young poet to leave. Shelley, though, was clearly in very low spirits, and a few days later he did actually attempt suicide by taking a huge dose of laudanum. Fortunately, a friend was on hand and got a doctor to him before his condition became serious.

These dramatic declarations of love completely overcame any lingering doubts young Mary might have had about obeying her father rather than taking up with the impetuous poet. When Shelley sent a further note proposing they elope, she did not hesitate for a moment. The date for their departure was duly set for the night of July 27.

The dash from Godwin's home to Dover, where the pair of young lovers planned to cross to the Continent, was a nightmare. The weather was overbearingly hot and Mary was ill for much of the time. The couple's anxiety was made all the worse by the fear — completely justified — that Mrs Godwin, an early riser, would learn of their departure and set off in hot pursuit. In fact, Shelley and Mary were only just at sea before the arrival of the furious stepmother at the port.

Once safely across the Channel, however, the lovers spent an idyllic month wandering through France and into

Switzerland, seeing the sights and living simply to conserve their dwindling funds. However, it was obvious that neither of them could lead the life of vagabonds for long, and by the end of August they had decided to return to England and try to effect a reconciliation with Godwin and separation from Harriet. After a far from comfortable crossing, they reached London tired and hungry on September 13. The bad news that greeted them was that Shelley had exhausted his bank account while they were away. It was a fact that was to colour their days through the ensuing winter, as Newman White has described:

> The story of that period is a rather monotonous chronicle of fruitless attempts to raise money, dodge bailiffs, and reach an understanding with Harriet, made tolerable for Shelley only by finding his new love a recompense for the loss of friendships and freedom of action.

As Shelley scratched around his acquaintances and business associates trying to raise the money to keep a roof over their heads and food in their mouths, Mary did her best to heal the breach with her father. However, Godwin was still smarting from the fact that his disciple and his daughter should have so totally ignored his words of wisdom, and therefore refused to see or assist either of them.

To occupy herself, Mary began keeping a diary of these grey days, and it makes uninspiring reading with its bleak picture of the two young lovers hounded on all sides, worried and frequently ill, and able to do little more than read and keep a wary eye open for creditors and bailiffs. Her generally uninspired prose is, though, raised a degree on December 6 when she learns that Harriet has given birth to a son on November 30. She comments wryly on the event as Shelley, torn by emotion, hurries off to see his child — for she is aware that she herself is now pregnant.

Christmas comes and goes with little change in the routine, although one or two of the couple's few remaining friends do visit them and try to cheer them up. On December 26 and 27, neither of them is particularly well and on the latter night, Mary notes in her diary that Shelley had an 'odd dream'. The next day, December 28, however, both seem a little better and decide on a rare night out. I quote the relevant extract from Mary's diary:

> *Wednesday, December 28* — Shelley and Clara out all the morning. Read *French Revolution* in the evening. Shelley and I go to Gary's Inn to get Hogg; he is not there; go to Arundel Street; can't find him. Go to Garnerin's. Lecture on electricity; the gases, and the phantasmagoria; return at half-past 9. Shelley goes to sleep. Read *View of French Revolution* till 12; go to bed.

To the harassed young poet and his mistress, the day no doubt seemed much like any other in what had been a most depressing winter. It may well have momentarily raised Shelley's spirits to hear about his old love, electricity, but it was only a brief diversion from their real problem which was still far from resolved.

However, unknown to either of them, the visit to Garnerin's *had* provided an experience which was to be of some importance when, their minds freed from this round of troubles, they returned to more creative pursuits. Just how influential that lecture and the man who gave it were to prove on Mary when she came to write her great novel, *Frankenstein*, is something we shall examine next.

5

A Display of Pyrotechnics

The Andrew Crosse who mounted the small lecture platform at Garnerin's on the night of Wednesday, December 28, 1814 was a far cry from the youth who had been the instigator of so many pranks during his days at Oxford and the high-living social entertainer of early manhood. His dedication to science, and the isolated life he had subsequently been living in Somerset, had turned him into a quietly-spoken, reserved and almost shy man of thirty. A contemporary report described him as being tall, light complexioned and with a frank and open-hearted manner. 'His address was not polished,' says this account, 'he appeared that which indeed he stated himself to be, the child of seclusion, devoted to scientific pursuit.'

The audience in the hall were still blinking in the glow of the heightened gas lights as Crosse appeared on the platform. His address had been preceded by a magic lantern display, the 'Phantasmagoria' to which Mary Shelley referred in her diary, in which a variety of amusing and instructive slides had been projected onto a screen behind the podium. The novelty of this invention — the precursor of the modern cinema — made all such demonstrations very popular with Londoners, and the commentary which had conducted the audience on a colourful journey to the far corners of the earth, shown them dramatic reconstructions of great moments in history, and finally illustrated some comic public and domestic situations, had been greeted at its conclusion with rapturous applause.

Andrew Crosse was introduced to the audience in the briefest manner, his name having already been posted on placards outside Garnerin's and inside the hall with the information that he was an electrician from Somerset speaking on 'Electricity and the Elements'. It was stated that he had been researching on the electricity of the atmosphere for some years and the first details of this work had been published just recently in Mr George Singer's much acclaimed book, *Elements of Electricity and Electro-Chemistry*. It was to Mr Singer that the audience had to be grateful, for persuading Mr Crosse to leave his wild and lovely retreat in Somerset to address it this evening. Mr Singer had called his friend Mr Crosse 'a most active and intelligent electrician' who had made numerous and remarkable observations with his extensive atmospherical conductor, about which he was now going to speak.

Crosse had decided against bringing any of his apparatus up to London to use during his lecture: primarily because of its heavy and cumbersome nature, and also because it would have been difficult to arrange any kind of set up which would adequately represent what he was doing at Fyne Court. Instead, he contented himself with a blackboard and a piece of chalk. As he had been something of a draughtsman in his youth, he was confident he could competently draw all the pieces of equipment necessary to explain what he was saying. One contemporary report makes a particular mention of the fact that his 'communication was unaccompanied by any apparatus, or any other way of describing his discoveries' and goes on: 'Yet his mode of explanation, his enthusiastic delivery ... wrought conviction in the mind of every one present.'

When the audience had finally settled themselves again and were giving him their attention, Crosse began to speak. At first he was hesitant, as one would expect of a man making his first important speech in public, but he gained in confidence as he found himself engaging and then exciting his listeners' interest. He opened his remarks by

One of the first books to carry details of Andrew Crosse's electrical experiments, Lectures on Electricity, *by Henry M. Noad (1849).*

declaring that he had dedicated his life to one great object — the theory of electricity, atmospheric electricity in particular, and that part of his work had been to imitate some of nature's productions.

At his home on top of the Quantocks in Somerset, he said, he had been carrying out experiments on a large scale with a network of electric wires supported and insulated on poles fixed to some of the tallest trees which stood in his grounds. This network of wires stretched as far as the eye could see and enabled him to conduct streams of lightning wherever he chose, even into his own home and laboratory. Quickly, he turned to the blackboard and sketched the pattern of the wires, showing how they all connected with his 'electric room'.

The audience were now clearly engrossed as Crosse went on to explain how he achieved this marvellous feat of 'capturing' natural electricity. His network consisted of a mile and a quarter of copper wire, and it was insulated on the poles by means of special funnels. Turning again to his blackboard, he deftly sketched one of the insulators (see diagram) as he went on to describe it:

Each of these funnels is made of copper about four and a half inches in diameter, and eleven inches in length, and into a cavity or socket of about two inches deep formed at the closed end of the funnel is firmly cemented a stout glass rod of sufficient length to reach to the open end of the funnel, where it is mounted, by means of strong cement, with a metallic cap and staple. The latter appendage receives the hook of a very strong wire, which passes through a circular plate of copper placed about four inches from the mouth of the funnel, and terminates in a hook to which one end of the exploring wire is fixed. The object of the metallic disc is to preclude the admission of snow, rain, etc., and thus to preserve the glass rod in a dry insulating condition.

Crosse proceeded to say that these funnels were easily raised to the tops of the poles by an arrangement of pulleys, and thus the wires could be drawn up and taken down as required. Outside the window of the gallery of his electrical laboratory a stout pole was erected firmly in the ground, on

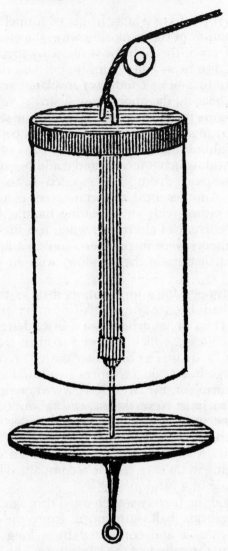

Andrew Crosse's electrical insulator.

top of which was fixed a large insulated funnel. This formed the termination of the exploring wire, the electricity being conveyed from it through the window by means of a stout wire to a large brass ball. From here it was conveyed by a curved wire to a brass conductor insulated and fixed on a table, and bearing the appropriate words, '*Noli me tangere*'.

On the same plane with the conductor, he said, was fixed another arrangement having a metallic communication with a neighbouring pond, and by means of a screw the brass ball with which it terminated could be adjusted at any required distance from the opposed brass ball of the conductor. Another most important piece of apparatus was a lever furnished with an insulating handle, by means of which the current of electricity, when too strong, or when no experiments were in progress, could easily be directed into the earth outside the window, without entering the room.

Crosse stopped for a moment, as if to let the import of what he had been saying sink into the minds of his audience. Then he launched into a brief description of his electrical battery, which he said consisted of 50 jars, containing 73 square feet of surface coated on one side only.

'To charge it,' he said, 'requires two hundred and thirty vigorous turns of the wheel of a twenty-inch cylinder electrical machine. Nevertheless, with about one-third of a mile of the wire, I have frequently collected sufficient electricity to charge and discharge this battery twenty times in a minute. And,' he paused as if he could still hear the sound ringing in his ears, 'this is accompanied by reports as loud of those of a cannon!'

Crosse said the battery was charged through the medium of a large brass ball, suspended from the ceiling immediately over it and connected by a long wire to the conductor in the gallery of the laboratory. The ball could be raised up and down from the battery by means of a long silk cord running over a pulley in the ceiling. He continued with a wave of his hand:

With this arrangement, I can, while sitting calmly at my study table, view the wonderful powers of this fearful agent, so awful to an ordinary observer, without danger. I can conduct the lightning in any required direction, and employ it to fuse wires, decompose fluids, *or fire inflammable substances*. And as I possess complete control over it, should the effects become too powerful, or if I merely wish to end the experiment, I can with a simple motion of my hand connect the insulated wire with the ground, and transmit the accumulated electricity instantly, with silence and safety, from my presence.

There were little sounds of astonishment from some sections of the audience as Crosse finished speaking, and from a few of the older, white-bearded gentlemen — clearly scientists or men well informed about scientific matters — a small burst of applause. Percy Shelley, with his knowledge of electricity, would certainly have been among those impressed with such information, and more than likely conveyed his admiration to the young girl by his side. In fact, I believe, she was already unconsciously absorbing information that was to prove of great use to her a short while later.

To everyone in Garnerin's that night, it was clear that this unassuming young man from Somerset had certainly achieved a quite remarkable control of electrical power. Yet what was the purpose of the magician's cave of equipment he had assembled to harness the wrath of the elements? Andrew Crosse was now going to enlighten them.

The speaker said that his experiments with the network of wires and batteries had produced a number of conclusions. The first was that in the usual state of the atmosphere, the electricity was invariably positive. Secondly, rain, fog, hail and sleet produced alterations of the electric state of the wire. It was usually negative when they first appeared, but often changed to positive, increasing and decreasing every three of four minutes. He believed these phenomena were so constant that whenever negative electricity was observed in the apparatus it was a sign that one or other of these weather conditions was imminent.

Thirdly, said Andrew Crosse, the approach of a charged cloud produced sometimes positive and at other times negative signs at first. Fourthly, a thick fog or driving rain could electrify the apparatus almost as much as a thunder cloud, while his fifth point was that in cloudy weather weak positive electricity usually prevailed, unless rain fell, in which case it became negative. Sixth, the positive electricity registered in clear, frosty weather was stronger than on a fine summer's day. He added as a rider that the strongest electrical atmosphere obviously occurred during a thunderstorm, while the weakest of all was found during the prevalence of north-easterly winds: that period when the atmosphere was considered particularly unhealthy, producing a sensation of dryness or extreme cold which was not, though, accompanied by a corresponding depression of the thermometer.

From all his observations, Crosse said, he had concluded, 'The usual positive electricity is weakest during the night. It increases with the sunrise, decreases towards the middle of the day, and increases as the sun declines. It then again diminishes and remains weak through the night.'

His work with the exploring wires had also given him a particular insight into the mysteries and construction of that terror of the weather, a thunder cloud, and he now proceeded to give an account of this to his still hushed and very attentive audience.

On the approach of a thunder cloud to the insulated atmospheric wire, the conductor attached to it, which is screwed into a table in my electrical room, gives corresponding signs of electrical action. In fair cloudy weather the atmospheric electricity is invariably positive, increasing in intensity at sun-rise and sun-set, and diminishing at mid-day and mid-night, varying as the evaporation of the moisture in the air. But when the thunder cloud (which appears to be formed by an unusually powerful evaporation, arising either from a scorching sun succeeding much wet, or vice versa) draws near, the pith balls suspended from the conductor open wide, with either positive or negative electricity; and when the edge of the cloud is perpendicular to the exploring wire, a slow succession of discharges takes place between the brass ball of the conductor and one of equal size, carefully connected with the nearest spot of moist ground.

I usually connect a large jar with the conductor which increases the force of, and in some degree regulates the number of the explosions; and the two balls between which the discharges pass can be easily regulated, as to their distance from each other, by a screw.

After a certain number of explosions, say of negative electricity which at first may be nine or ten in a minute, a cessation occurs of some seconds or minutes, as the case may be, when about an equal number of explosions of positive electricity takes place, of similar force to the former, *indicating the passage of two oppositely and equally electrified zones of cloud*: then follows a second zone of negative electricity, occasioning several more discharges in a minute than from either of the first pair of zones; which rate of increase appears to vary according to the size and power of the cloud.

The speaker raised his right arm slightly and then dropped it dramatically onto the podium.

Then occurs another cessation, followed by an equally powerful series of discharges of positive electricity, indicating the passage of a second pair of zones: These, in like manner, are followed by others, fearfully increasing the rapidity of the discharges, when a *regular stream commences*, interrupted only by the change into the opposite electricities. The intensity of each new pair of zones is greater than that of the former, as may be proved by removing the two balls to a greater distance from each other.

When the centre of the cloud is vertical to the wire, the greatest effect consequently takes place, during which the *windows rattle in their frames*, and the bursts of thunder without, and noise within, every now and then accompanied with a crash of accumulated fluid in the wire, striving to get free between the balls, produce the most awful effect, which is not a little increased by the pauses occasioned by the interchange of zones. Great caution must, of course, be observed during this interval, or the consequences would be fatal.

Once again Crosse's audience found themselves open-mouthed, and many looked with surprise from one to another to see if they had all been affected in the same way. It was certainly proving to be a fascinating and even unnerving lecture! The speaker continued:

As the cloud passes onward, the opposite portions of the

65

zones, which first affected the wire, come into play, and the effect is weakened with each successive pair till all dies away, and not enough electricity remains in the atmosphere to affect a gold-leaf electrometer. I have remarked that the air is remarkably free of electricity, at least more so than usual, both before and after the passage of one of these clouds. Sometimes, a little previous to a storm, the gold leaves connected with the conductor will, for many hours, open and shut rapidly, as if they were panting, evidently showing a great electrical disturbance.

Without pausing, Andrew Crosse volunteered the information that when his battery was fully charged by such a thunder cloud, it would fuse 30 feet of iron wire into red hot balls. When connected with 3,000 feet of exploring wire during a storm, it was charged instantaneously and fully.

Just as quickly, though, he added:

> As I am fearful of destroying the jars of my battery, I connect the two opposite coatings of the battery with brass balls, one inch in diameter, and place at such distance from each other as to cause a discharge. When the middle of a thunder cloud is over head, a crashing stream of discharges takes place between the balls, the effect of which must be witnessed to be conceived.

Now Andrew Crosse took a breath and looked down at the few pages of notes before him on the podium. He had nearly reached the end of his lecture. He looked at the crowd of faces staring up at him with rapt attention: he could not restrain a little smile of satisfaction from creeping across his face. Their enjoyment of his lecture was obvious to see; and the amazement at what he had revealed seemed equally evident. He could not remember feeling such a sense of satisfaction since those days of his youth when one of his electrical pranks had worked. This, though, was a very different kind of triumph. This was the triumph of the scientist finding acceptance for the work to which he had dedicated his life.

He considered that he had now said enough about the facts of his work to satisfy both the scientists and the laymen in the audience. He knew there was much more that would be of interest to other electricians, but it was of a technical nature that would probably go above the heads of the rest of his listeners. It would be best to leave such details to another occasion: perhaps one attended only by scientists. After thanking the audience for their kind attention, Crosse decided to end with a personal story of a rather magnificent spectacle that he had witnessed during the course of his work at Fyne Court, one winter evening a year or two back during a dense fog. It concerned the sort of electrical phenomena that might be familiar to his audience; but none of them could have had quite the same experience as this:

I was sitting in my electrical room on a dark November day during a very dense, driving fog and rain which had prevailed for many hours, sweeping over the earth, impelled by a south-west wind. The mercury in the barometer was low, and the thermometer indicated a low temperature.

I had at this time 1,600 feet of wire insulated which crossed two small valleys, and brought the electric fluid into my room. There were four insulators, and each of them was streaming with wet, from the effects of the driving fog. From about eight o'clock in the morning until four in the afternoon, not the least appearance of electricity was visible at the atmospheric conductor, even by the most careful application of the condenser and multiplier; indeed, so effectually did the exploring wire conduct away the electricity which was communicated to it, that when it was connected by means of a copper wire with the prime conductor of my 18-inch cylinder in high action, and a gold leaf electrometer placed in contact with the connecting wire, not the slightest effect was produced upon the gold leaves.

Having given up the trial of further experiments upon it, I took a book, and occupied myself with reading, leaving by chance the receiving ball at upwards of an inch distance from the ball in the atmospheric conductor. About four o'clock in the afternoon, whilst I was still reading, I suddenly heard a very strong explosion between the two balls, and shortly after many more took place, until they became one interrupted stream of explosions, which died away and re-commenced with the opposite electricity in equal violence. The stream of fire was too vivid to look at for any length of time, and the effect was most splendid, and continued without intermission, save that occasioned by the interchange of electricities *for upwards of five hours*, and then ceased totally.

During the whole day, and a great part of the succeeding night, there was no material change in the barometer, thermometer, hygrometer, or wind; nor did the driving fog and rain alter in its violence. The wind was not high, but blew steadily from the S.W. Had it not been for my exploring wire, I should not have had the least idea of such an electrical accumulation in the atmosphere: the least contact with the conductor would have *occasioned instant death* — the stream of fluid far exeeding anything I ever witnessed, excepting during a thunderstorm.

Had the insulators been dry, what would have been the effect? In every acre of fog there was enough of accumulated electricity to have destroyed every animal within that acre. How can this be accounted for? How much have we to learn before we can boast of understanding this intricate science?

For just a moment, as Andrew Crosse collected up his sheaf of papers and began to leave the platform, there was absolute silence in the auditorium. The silence of an audience that had been intrigued, informed and — particularly — fascinated by the man they had been listening to. Then hands began to clap and an increasing chorus of bravos echoed through the hall.

The electrician from Somerset smiled shyly, but with pleasure glowing all over his face, as he walked down the aisle to the back of the hall. Some members of the audience were on their feet clapping in his direction as he passed, and there were even a few hands reached out to pat him on the back.

Crosse knew the lecture had been a personal triumph, and he was glad now he had allowed himself to be talked into making it — even if he had had to tear himself away from his family at the festive time of the year.

He inclined his head slightly to acknowledge the applause as he passed the last few rows of chairs and disappeared out of the hall. As he passed the row where the young Percy Shelley and Mary Godwin sat, they, too, joined in the acclaim. Perhaps the eyes of the scientist met with those of the girl who, two years later, was to amaze the world of literature with a book that took for its theme the idea of an inanimate human being brought to life through the power of electricity.

The purpose of his visit to London now over, Crosse returned quickly to the peace and isolation of the Quantocks, and to the obscurity which was to confine him for almost another quarter of a century, when he seemingly unlocked the greatest of all human mysteries: the secret of life. At the same time, he was to find himself labelled as being no better than the man at the heart of Mary Godwin's book: the book which I believe he in part inspired. The wheel — as we shall see — had turned full circle. Fact, which had been utilised and re-shaped for fiction, had then incredibly become fact itself once again ...

6

The Frankenstein Connection

It is my belief that Mary Shelley was profoundly impressed by Andrew Crosse's address that December night in Garnerin's lecture hall, and that what she heard played an influential part in the construction of her novel *Frankenstein*. I believe that some of the character of the electrician from Somerset is to be found in the figure of Victor Frankenstein himself, the man who creates life, but that he is also more specifically portrayed in the guise of a lecturer, Dr Waldman, of Ingolstadt University, who first fires the young Frankenstein's imagination with the idea of trying to pierce the mysteries of creation. My reasons for this conviction I shall now explain.

The life of Percy Bysshe Shelley and his young mistress Mary Godwin after that depressing winter of 1814 is, of course, well known, and I think I need only briefly mention the most important details here: After a wretched January, in which their financial difficulties necessitated them changing their lodgings, Mary gave birth prematurely to a baby girl in February, 1815, but the child died a few days later. Another death, however, changed their fortunes somewhat — that of Shelley's grandfather, Sir Bysshe, and this gave him access to an inheritance of £800 per year which eased his immediate money problems. In August of that year, the young lovers moved out of a London which had never seemed very friendly towards them — in particular because of William Godwin's continued opposition to their liaison — and settled in a cottage at Bishopsgate near Windsor Park. Because of all his difficulties and the business of trying to settle matters with his wife Harriet, Shelley produced virtually no literary work at all at this time.

In the autumn of 1815, Shelley did feel inclined to begin work again. Mary, we also learn, was pregnant once more. That winter seemingly passed agreeably and quietly for both of them, and then on January 24, 1816, Mary went into labour and produced a bouncing, auburn-haired infant, William. Delighted though the poet was with his new child, his disillusionment with England was growing steadily, and he began to believe that the only chance he had of seeing his talent flourish was by going abroad. So in May he and Mary, along with Mary's stepsister, Clair Clairmont, left England for Geneva.

The early summer days that the young lovers spent by Lake Geneva were the happiest they had known, and whenever the weather was good they delighted in walking along the shores of the lake or boating over its smooth surface. Their happiness was increased all the more when the exiled poet, Lord Byron, came to live beside the lake at the Villa Diodati, and from then on Shelley and he were in each other's company almost constantly. There was one other person in the group, Dr John Polidori, Byron's young physician and travelling companion.

Unfortunately, however, the good weather did not continue for long, and soon the group were confined indoors while rain lashed the lake and countryside outside.* To amuse themselves, the party began reading aloud ghost stories from a book which had been found in the library of the Villa Diodati entitled *Fantasmagoriana, ou Recueil d'histoires d'apparitions, de spectres, etc.*, a French translation from the

---

* According to several accounts of this period, a terrible thunderstorm broke over the lake on the night of June 13, and it has been suggested that this display of lightning was responsible for the idea of the group writing ghost stories. If this is the case, the storm might also have reminded Mary of Crosse's lecture on the power of electricity in the elements and subconsciously started her mind working towards the idea which became *Frankenstein*.

The Villa Diodati on the shores of Lake Geneva where Mary Shelley began to write Frankenstein.

Lord Byron. He was host to the Shelleys during their stay in Switzerland.

German which had been published about 1810. The effect of these grim little tales on a group of people as highly strung and imaginative as Shelley, Byron, Mary Godwin, Claire Clairmont and the mercurial Polidori can be imagined. Mary Shelley leaves us in no doubt about this when she recalls the anthology in the Introduction she later wrote for *Frankenstein*, describing the origin of her novel.

There was 'The History of the Inconstant Lover' who, when he thought to clasp the bride to whom he had pledged his vows, found himself in the arms of the pale ghost of her whom he had deserted. There was the tale of the sinful founder of his race, whose miserable doom it was to bestow the kiss of death on all the younger sons of his fated house, just when they reached the age of promise. His gigantic, shadowy form, clothed like the ghost in Hamlet, in complete armour, but with the beaver up, was seen at midnight, by the moon's fitful beams, to advance slowly along the gloomy avenue. The shape was lost beneath the shadow of the castle walls; but soon a gate swung back, a step was heard, the door of the chamber opened, and he advanced to the couch of the blooming youths, cradled in healthy sleep. Eternal sorrow sat upon his face as he bent down and kissed the forehead of the boys, who from that hour withered like flowers snapt upon the stalk. I have not seen these stories since then; but their incidents are as fresh in my mind as if I had read them yesterday.

According to the biographies of both Byron and Shelley, a long discussion of the book and its horrors took place among the members of the group as they huddled around the fireplace in the Villa Diodati during the night of June 16. Nor did this exhaust the subject, for Mary records that the talk continued again by candlelight two nights later. On this occasion, Newman White tells us in *Shelley*, Byron referred especially to a poem recently published by Coleridge entitled 'Christabel' which made a particular use of this kind of material.

He [Byron] quoted the lines describing the horrible secret of the witch's deformity. For a moment there was silence; then Shelley, who had been staring at Mary, uttered a sudden shriek, pressed his hands over his head, seized a candle, and fled from the room. It required Polidori's professional services with cold water and ether to restore him to anything like normality. As he looked at Mary he had been shocked into uncontrollable horror by seeing a vision of a woman he had once heard of who had eyes for nipples.

In such an excited atmosphere, it seemed the most natural thing in the world when Byron proposed to his fellow *literarti*, 'We will each write a ghost story.' Turning to Mary he added, 'You and I will publish ours together.'

Despite such an outstanding array of assembled talents, the high hopes that some truly remarkable stories might result were not fulfilled. Byron began a tale entitled *The Assassins* which he did not complete and which appeared later as a fragment printed at the end of his poem *Mazeppa*. Shelley also commenced a fanciful story based on the experiences of his early life, but this quickly foundered as his enthusiasm waned. Polidori, we are told, had 'some terrible idea about a skull-headed lady, who was so punished for peeping through a keyhole', but likewise did not get far with it. He is, though, said to have worked on another story about vampires which was later completed and published as *The Vampyre*. It was at first described as the work of Lord Byron and no doubt this contributed to its popularity. Later, Polidori received the credit due him and the tale is rightly regarded today as perhaps the first great vampire story.

Byron, it seems, did not follow up his generous offer to help Mary with her contribution, and, as she admitted later, she was soon struggling to find inspiration.

I busied myself to think of a story — a story to rival those which had excited us to this task. One which would speak to the mysterious fears of our nature, and awaken thrilling horror — one to make the reader dread to look round, to curdle the blood, and quicken the beatings of the heart. If I did not accomplish these things, my ghost story would be unworthy of its name. I thought and pondered — vainly. I felt that blank incapability of invention which is the greatest misery of authorship, when dull Nothing replies to our anxious invocations. Have you thought of a story? I was asked each

74

morning, and each morning I was forced to reply with a mortifying negative.

Mary knew that she had to find a concept which would fire her imagination. 'Invention,' she later stated, 'consists in the capacity of seizing on the capabilities of a subject, and in the power of moulding and fashioning ideas suggested to it.'

The poet's young mistress had made a point of always listening silently whenever Shelley and Byron were deep in conversation, and it was during one of their discussions on the principle of life and whether there was any probability of its ever being discovered, that the germ of a story was at last sown in her mind. As she later wrote in her Introduction:

> They talked of the experiments of Dr Darwin (I speak not of what the Doctor really did, or said that he did, but, as more to my purpose, of what was then spoken of as having been done by him) who preserved a piece of vermicelli in a glass case, till by some extraordinary means it began to move with voluntary motion. Not thus, after all, would life be given. Perhaps a corpse would be re-animated; galvanism had given token of such things: perhaps the component parts of a creature might be manufactured, brought together, and endued with vital warmth.

There was the idea, she thought excitedly to herself, the creation of a man and his re-animation! It was the early hours of the morning before this conversation finished, and when Mary went up to bed she found the idea buzzing around in her mind, and she was quite unable to sleep.

> My imagination, unbidden, possessed and guided me, gifting the successive images that arose in my mind with a vividness far beyond the usual bounds of reverie. I saw — with shut eyes, but acute mental vision, — I saw the pale student of unhallowed arts kneeling beside the thing he had put together. I saw the hideous phantasm of a man stretched out, and then, on the

75

working of some powerful engine,* show signs of life, and stir with an uneasy, half vital motion. Frightful must it be; for supremely frightful would be the effect of any human endeavour to mock the stupendous mechanism of the Creator of the world. His success would terrify the artist; he would rush away from his odious handywork, horror-stricken. He would hope that, left to itself the slight spark of life which he had communicated would fade; that this thing, which had received such imperfect animation would subside into dead matter; and he might sleep in that belief that the silence of the grave would quench for ever the transient existence of the hideous corpse which he had looked upon as the cradle of life. He sleeps; but he is awakened; he opens his eyes; behold the horrid thing stands at his bedside, opening his curtains, and looking on him with yellow, watery, but speculative eyes.

The young girl — she was barely nineteen, remember — was literally possessed by her idea. She shuddered with fright and quickly ran to the window and threw it open to assure herself that she had only been dreaming. As she stared at the glassy surface of Lake Geneva in the moonlight and the high, white peaks of the Alps beyond, she knew she had found the theme for her story: all it needed now was the details.

Swift as light, and as cheering, was the idea that broke in on me. 'I have found it! what terrified me will terrify others; and I need only describe the spectre which had haunted my midnight pillow.' On the morrow I announced that I had thought of a story. I began that day with the words, 'It was on a dreary night of November,' making only a transcript of the grim terrors of my waking dream.

We know for a *fact* that Mary intended *Frankenstein* to be only a short story — as had been proposed for all the writers — and that what she first composed now forms Chapter Five of the book. It was Shelley who, when he saw and liked

---

* It has been suggested by more than one authority that this 'powerful engine' could well be a large galvanic battery. If this is the case, it can be seen as another small link in the association with Andrew Crosse because he, of course, devised and used such batteries in almost all his experiments and spoke about them during the course of his lecture at Garnerin's.

this episode, encouraged her to expand it into a full-length novel. What is open to discussion are her sources for the details of the story — and this is where my claim for Andrew Crosse comes in.

As we have learned, inspiration came in part from the dream, in part from the conversations between Byron and Shelley which ranged across the current theories on the origin of life, the experiments in galvanism, and the wonders of electricity. However, I believe inspiration came also from that impressive lecture by Andrew Crosse on electricity, whose details must have opened young Mary's eyes to just some of the miracles it might be possible to achieve in the future through its agency.

Modern science was very much in its infancy at the start of the nineteenth century, although its enormous possibilities were beginning to be realised in the work of scientists like Darwin, Davy and Michael Faraday. Electricity was particularly prominent in scientific research, and there were certain theories already being advanced at this time that the 'divine spark' of life might be electrical or at least quasi-electrical in nature. We shall see how Mary utilised this idea in her work later.

Another important part of my argument that Crosse was involved in this creative process is the fact that Mary not only heard him speak, but heard him *spoken of* on at least one other occasion. The man who spoke of him was Robert Southey, the poet and essayist, who is perhaps best remembered as a friend of two other great poets of this era, Coleridge and Wordsworth. Southey was born of an old Somerset family in Bristol in 1774, and retained strong connections with the West Country throughout his life — which resulted in his acquaintanceship with Crosse. He lost his father when he was very young, and while still a schoolboy we learn that he often used to spend his holidays with an uncle who lived in Taunton, and this doubtless gave him his introduction to the Quantocks which proved a source of delight to him.

Despite the sedateness of much of his later life, Southey was something of a rebel as a young man, and like so many of his generation was profoundly influenced by reading

Robert Southey, the poet and essayist, who knew both Mary Shelley and Andrew Crosse, and talked of the Somerset electrician's work.

Godwin's *Political Justice*. In 1794 Southey by chance met Samuel Taylor Coleridge and found that the young poet also shared his republican sympathies, so together the two men planned a new life-style to be known as Pantisocracy. The idea was simple: a group of young men were to emigrate to America and there found an agricultural community in which everything was to be held in common. All of them had to be married, it was decided, and taking the first step in this design, he and Coleridge married Edith and Sara Fricker in 1795. However, for various reasons this was about as far as the scheme got, and although the two young men continued to discuss the idea, their resolution declined with each passing month.

Even so, Southey still felt himself at odds with society, and therefore took himself and his wife, Edith, off to Portugal where he was proposing to write a book on the country. By the time he returned he had come to terms with himself and knew dreams of America, of Pantisocracy and a carefree existence were not those for a married man. He had to make a steady living and decided on a career as a barrister. This desire for the law did not stay with him for long.

For a short while he remained in London, where he met William Godwin and his wife, but city life was not really to his taste and he decided to move to Keswick, not far from where he knew Coleridge was now living. His health, which had never been good, made it imperative for him to get plenty of exercise and fresh air, and in 1799 we hear of him taking a walking holiday in the Quantocks. During one of his expeditions, Reverend William Greswell says in his *The Land of Quantock* (1918), he stopped at Fyne Court in Broomfield and met the Crosse family. Young Andrew, though, was away at this time, and did not hear of the visit until he returned.

For the next few years, Southey eked out a precarious existence mainly through journalistic contributions and some books on historical subjects. Then in 1805 he published the first of his epic poems, *Madoc*, and the flowering of his reputation began. In the following year, 1806, he took another walking holiday in Somerset,

Reverend Greswell tells us, and once again his steps took him to Fyne Court. There was a new master of Fyne Court now (both of the older Crosses were dead), and Southey took an immediate liking to the rather melancholy but industrious young Andrew Crosse. Finding Southey a sympathetic listener, Crosse regaled him with stories of the electrical experiments he was then beginning to carry out. Already he had started work on constructing the network of copper wires strung out on poles across the grounds to draw electricity to his laboratory and, before continuing on his journey, Southey was treated to an impressive display with this equipment. Although not a man of great vision, Southey could not help but be made aware of the importance that electricity was going to have in the future. For many years after, the thought remained with him as to how incongruous it was that such pioneer work should be going on in the isolated home of a young Somersetshire squire.

With the coming of his fame, Southey confined himself almost completely to his home, Greta Hall in Keswick, and in 1813 his stature as a poet was recognised with his appointment as Poet Laureate. It was here also that, as we have already seen, a young man had suddenly presented himself at his door in 1811 and introduced himself as Percy Shelley. The young poet was then 19 and had recently rashly married Harriet Westbrook.

Shelley had come seeking Southey because he considered him 'a really great man' and because he believed him to be a radical and free thinker like himself. Southey, however, had to disillusion the poet: by now he had lost the desire to change the world through Pantisocracy and his politics were strongly Conservative. Shelley went away disappointed, preferring to remember the ageing man as he imagined he must have been in his youth. (Like Shelley, Southey had also come into conflict with authority in his youth. He was expelled from Westminster College for writing an article about his Jacobin principles for a magazine evocatively entitled *The Flagellant*!)

Only once again did the two men come face to face and this is the crucial meeting as far as our story is concerned. It happened in the late autumn of 1814, when Southey made one of his rare visits up to London and accidentally heard something of the dire straits his former admirer was in. He went to see Shelley and his young mistress in the hope that he might be able to help in some way. According to Thomas Love Peacock in his *Memoirs of Shelley* (1909), there was little practical support that Southey could offer, but the two men did spend some hours in enjoyable conversation. Their talk ranged over a variety of subjects and predictably took in the current fascination with chemistry and electricity, in which Shelley was greatly interested, of course. Southey, though, had only the slightest interest in such matters and was only able to contribute to the conversation his story of a visit to an electrician named Andrew Crosse who was working with some extraordinary equipment in the fastness of the Quantock Hills. In time the talk became desultory and Southey decided it was time to leave.

Throughout his visit, he had barely been conscious of the young Mary Godwin sitting quietly in the corner of the room while they talked. However, he left with the distinct impression that she had not missed a word they had said. (Southey, as we shall later see, was also to meet Andrew Crosse again in a most fateful meeting on the Quantock Hills in 1837, when he became the first person to hear the story of the electrician's amazing discovery of live insects as a result of one of his experiments.)

It is my belief that Mary had *certainly* been aware of everything that had been mentioned in the conversation between Southey and Shelley. She had already evidenced a strong pleasure at just listening to her lover when he talked, and also shown that she retained and learned much from what was said. I think the Andrew Crosse story first entered her consciousness right there and then. When she heard him actually speak in person the following December, his character was imprinted on her subconscious once and for all — to be drawn upon when the idea for her story arose, and she cast round — as any writer does — for the characters to people her plot.

So, with these elements of the creation of *Frankenstein* I trust established, how does Crosse feature in the book? As I indicated at the start of the chapter, I think there is something of Crosse in the character of Frankenstein himself: he is presented as an enthusiastic, dedicated and bold student of science like Crosse, and like him, too, is obsessed with the 'spark of life', electricity. More particularly, though, I see Crosse as the figure of Dr Waldman, the science lecturer at Ingolstadt University, which Victor Frankenstein attends. He has been aged, certainly, but he speaks to his pupil, the young Frankenstein, in the same manner and with the same conviction that the man from the depths of Somerset employed when addressing his lecture to the audience at Garnerin's.

To begin with, there is an episode in Chapter Two of Mary's book which describes how Frankenstein becomes fascinated with the subjects of electricity and galvanism. The 'man of great research' who is mentioned could so easily have some of Crosse in him. Let me quote the relevant passages:

> When I was about fifteen years old we had retired to our house near Belrive, when we witnessed a most violent and terrible thunder storm. It advanced from behind the mountains of Jura; and the thunder burst at once with frightful loudness from various quarters of the heavens. I remained, while the storm lasted, watching its progress with curiosity and delight. As I stood at the door, on a sudden I beheld a stream of fire issue from an old and beautiful oak, which stood about twenty yards from our house; and so soon as the dazzling light vanished, the oak had disappeared and nothing remained but a blasted stump. When we visited it the next morning, we found the tree shattered in a singular manner. It was not splintered by the shock, but entirely reduced to thin ribands of wood. I never beheld any thing so utterly destroyed.
>
> Before this I was not unacquainted with the more obvious laws of electricity. On this occasion a man of great research in natural philosophy was with us, and, excited by this catastrophe, he entered on the explanation of a theory which he had formed on the subject of electricity and galvanism, which was at once new and astonishing to me. All that he said threw greatly into the shade Cornelius Agrippa, Albertus Magnus, and Paracelsus, the lords of my imagination; but by some

82

Frontispiece to an early edition of Frankenstein *published in 1831. The artist was T. Holst.*

fatality the overthrow of these men disinclined me to pursue my accustomed studies. It seemed to me as if nothing would or could ever be known. All that had so long engaged my attention suddenly grew despicable. By one of those caprices of the mind, which we are perhaps most subject to in early youth, I at once gave up my former occupations; set down natural history and all its progeny as a deformed and abortive creative creation; and entertained the greatest disdain for a would-be science, which could never ever step within the threshold of real knowledge. In this mood of mind I betook myself to the mathematics, and the branches of study appertaining to that science as being built upon secure foundations, and so worthy of my consideration. Thus strangely are our souls constructed, and by such slight ligaments are we bound to prosperity or ruin.

It was just such an observation that Crosse used as the basis for his first electrical experiments, and it was with similar enthusiasm that he conveyed how he set out with painstaking care to tread paths no one had previously followed in the fields of electrical research.

Now, let us look at Dr Waldman who seems closer still to our subject. Victor Frankenstein describes the professor, and the effect he has on his life, in Chapter Three:

Partly from curiosity, and partly from idleness, I went into the lecturing room, which M. Waldman entered shortly after. This professor was very unlike his colleagues. He appeared about fifty years of age, but with an aspect expressive of the greatest benevolence; a few grey hairs covered his temples, but those at the back of his head were nearly black. His person was short, but remarkably erect; and his voice the sweetest I had ever heard. He began his lecture by a recapitulation of the history of chemistry, and the various improvements made by different men of learning, pronouncing with fervour the names of the most distinguished discoverers. He then took a cursory view of the present state of the science, and explained many of its elementary terms. After having made a few preparatory experiments, he concluded with a panegyric upon modern chemistry, the terms of which I shall never forget:

'The ancient teachers of this science,' said he, 'promised impossibilities, and performed nothing. The modern masters promise very little; they know that metals cannot be transmuted, and that the elixir of life is a chimera. But these philosophers, whose hands seem only made to dabble in dirt, and their eyes to pore over the microscope or crucible, have indeed performed miracles. They penetrate into the recesses of nature, and show how she works in her hiding places. They ascend into the heavens: they have discovered how the blood circulates, and the nature of the air we breathe. They have acquired new and almost unlimited powers; they can

84

command the thunders of heaven, mimic the earthquake, and even mock the invisible world with its own shadows.'

Such were the professor's words — rather let me say such the words of fate, enounced to destroy me. As he went on, I felt as if my soul were grappling with a palpable enemy; one by one the various keys were touched which formed the mechanism of my being: chord after chord was sounded, and soon my mind was filled with one thought, one conception, one purpose. So much has been done, exclaimed the soul of Frankenstein — more, far more, will I achieve: treading in the steps already marked. I will pioneer a new way, explore unknown powers, and unfold to the world the deepest mysteries of creation.

On the following day, Frankenstein pays a visit to Professor Waldman and finds him 'even more mild and attractive than in public'. There was, said the student, 'a certain dignity in his mein during his lecture, which in his own house was replaced by the greatest affability and kindness'. Our hero then tells his teacher how impressed he was by his words and begs his guidance as to how he might pursue his objective:

'I am happy,' said M. Waldman, 'to have gained a disciple; and if your application equals your ability, I have no doubt of your success. Chemistry is that branch of natural philosophy in which the greatest improvements have been and may be made: it is on that account that I have made it my peculiar study; but at the same time I have not neglected the other branches of science. A man would make but a very sorry chemist if he attended to that department of human knowledge alone. If your wish is to become really a man of science, and not merely a petty experimentalist, I should advise you to apply to every branch of natural philosophy, including mathematics.'

He then took me into his laboratory, and explained to me the uses of his various machines; instructing me as to what I ought to procure, and promising me the use of his own when I should have advanced far enough in the science not to derange their mechanism. He also gave me the list of books which I had requested; and I took my leave.

Thus ended a day memorable to me: it decided my future destiny.

As Frankenstein continues his studies, he finds in

Waldman a true friend. 'His gentleness was never tinged by dogmatism; and his instructions were given with an air of frankness and good nature, that banished every idea of pedantry.' Not surprisingly, the professor takes great pleasure in his pupil's progress and when they finally part company, two years later, the older man feels the young man is assured of a great future. Whether he expected Frankenstein to achieve what he does is unlikely, and no doubt — like the reader — he would have felt a chill of horror at the words which our hero writes exultantly in Chapter Four: 'After days and nights of incredible labour and fatigue, I succeeded in discovering the cause of generation and life; nay, more, I became myself capable of bestowing animation from lifeless matter.' As readers of the novel will know, Waldman does not re-appear in the story again; just as after *his* fleeting appearance, Crosse never again came into contact with the Shelleys.

Such, then, is my evidence for 'The Frankenstein Connection'. It remains very much a personal conviction — although I believe it is backed up by some important evidence. It deserves, and will no doubt receive, much further discussion and investigation, for the whole question of the sources and origins of *Frankenstein* is one that has exercised the minds of scholars for well over a century and a half without showing any sign of abating.

However, when a final verdict is reached on this intriguing mystery, I feel sure Andrew Crosse will find a place somewhere in that definitive text. I trust, too, that it will not just be this element of his life that is remembered, for as I shall now go on to show, the remainder of his life was filled with much else that was fascinating, unusual and perhaps even more amazing still ...

7

'The Thunder and Lightning Man'

Although his lecture in London had been an undoubted success, Andrew Crosse had no desire to address further meetings, and the following day he said goodbye to his friend, George Singer, and hurried back to Somerset to see the New Year in with his family. Singer was naturally sorry that his fellow electrician would not stay longer, but as he himself was about to undertake a new series of lectures, to be followed by a trip to the Continent to supervise publication of the various editions of *Elements of Electricity and Electro-Chemistry*, he knew he could not offer to spend much time with Crosse. There were also some electrical experiments that he wanted to try and finish. So, reluctantly, the two men said goodbye after their brief time together and Crosse's coach sped off in the direction of the West Country. Neither man had the slightest idea that, sadly, it had been the very last time they would meet in person.

Once back at Fyne Court, Crosse did not for a moment yearn for the public acclaim or bright lights of London, and very quickly settled back into his life as a country squire and electrician. He put into operation a programme of renovation at Fyne Court and pressed on with his experiments. Despite his isolation, and his desire to preserve his privacy, he was not a man unaware or uninterested in what was happening in the world at large.

From his papers we can tell that one of his major sources of information was his former school companion, John Kenyon (1784–1856), who thanks to a considerable inheritance, was by the early part of the nineteenth century something of a philanthropist as well as a poet. In hindsight, it is possible to see that Kenyon's main importance in literature was the sustaining friendships that he conducted with a number of important poets including Coleridge, Southey and Browning. To Crosse, as well, he proved a good friend, concerned with the electrician's well-being, and corresponded with him frequently throughout his life. A passage from a typical letter from Crosse to Kenyon dated July 1815 illustrates their intimacy:

> I should like to see Bonaparte: if he lands at Plymouth I shall endeavour to get a peep at him. It must be gratifying to rest one's eyes upon a man who will live to the end of time, whose name will be in the mouths of all nations, when our bodies are mouldered to dust.

He achieved his ambition, for in her *Memoirs*, Cornelia Crosse reprints a short account her husband left of his trip to Plymouth:

> I left home on Wednesday morning about eight o'clock, reached Exeter on my mare about four o'clock, left Exeter ten o'clock same night, reached Plymouth Dock at half after five Thursday morning, saw Bonaparte about six o'clock same night. He started in the *Bellerophon*, without signal, at about one o'clock, Friday, August 4th, 1815, was met by a sloop-of-war, who exchanged signals with the *Bellerophon*; followed by the *Eurotus* frigate with French officers of rank aboard also by the [unnamed] and *Glasgow* frigate and *Mackerel* schooner. The *Bellerophon* bore eastward, and I followed her some hours; was on the water from twelve to two; sailed ten miles from dock, and about twenty-five or thirty in all. Saw Bonaparte between decks, afterwards, in the cabin window, the curtain of which was drawn by a French lady; got within thirty yards of him, and was told by Captain Maitland to keep off.

Increasingly, however, he spent longer periods in his laboratory and aside from the work on atmospheric electricity with his network of wires, he also became immersed in voltaic electricity and carried out many experiments on crystalline formations. Such trials had, of course, first commenced back in the early 1800s after the discovery of the remarkable agonite crystals in nearby Holwell Cavern. However, his major experimentation seems to have occurred in the years between 1815 and 1817, as Mrs Crosse tells us:

> By his close and ingenious imitation of Nature's arrangements, together with the application of electricity, he formed various metallic and earthy crystals, which had never before been formed by art, and in some instances he produced substances that have never been found combined in nature. I don't think Mr Crosse was at all impressed with the importance and interest attached to this discovery of these laws of nature.

The memoranda that Crosse left of his work at this period shows that he was working on 'forming mineral substances by slow electric action'. Believing the laws of form to be subject to certain molecular arrangements caused by electric attraction and repulsion, he experimented on the combination of substances under voltaic action, anticipating thereby the formation of crystals. He was clearly a man of great patience where his work was concerned, and Mrs Crosse tells us that the motto of his laboratory was 'It is better to follow nature blindfold than art with both eyes open.'

Details are still in existence of several of Crosse's experiments, but no purpose would, I think, be served by reprinting them in a popular biography such as this — suffice it for me to just include a section of his remarks on the conclusions he drew from this area of his work which, as I said, so absorbed him at this period:

> We have seen that a union of *electric action* with a moderately *uniform temperature*, and *sufficiency of heat* to prevent congelation of the fluid under action, absence of light, together with the interposition of a more or less *porous medium*, will attract the

89

crystallisable matter from its solution, and produce a variety of forms, which will not make their appearance without such conditions. We have likewise seen that those crystallisations or formations are greatly assisted by constant motion. Under these circumstances, I have produced about 200 varieties of minerals, exactly resembling in all respect similar ones found in nature, as well as some others never before discovered in nature or formed by art. A specimen which I have made of a *subsulphate of copper* is an instance of this.

Still, there are a vast number of minerals, which, in the present state of the science, defy the ingenuity of man to imitate, but many of which have been produced by *central or volcanic heat*, or *immense pressure* added to the other requisites. The thing to consider is, from what source does the required electric action arise?

Now, in answer to this, as far as we know, it most probably arises from one of the following causes: first, from terrestrial electric currents, caused by permanent magnetic action passing at right angles to them: or secondly, from similar electric currents excited by the union of vast strata of dissimilar rocks in contact with subterranean waters; or thirdly, from similar currents, either excited or aided by a central or volcanic heat, perhaps coming under the laws of thermo-electricity; or fourthly, and lastly, by *local electric action*. The following details exemplify what I mean by the latter, viz, local electric action.

Some years since, being at Weymouth, I observed some rounded limestones and some sea-shells embedded in the clay of a small perpendicular cliff, each stone and shell being covered with crystals of sulphate of lime. On looking around to investigate the cause of the formation of sulphate of lime upon these substances, I discovered a stratum of decomposing sulphuret of iron, running horizontally on the top of the cliff and just below the soil; accordingly, I reasoned thus: The rain water penetrating the soil moistened the sulphuret of iron, and decomposed it; the oxygen of the water converting the *sulphuret* to the *sulphate*; and the sulphate of iron, being a soluble salt, passed through the clay, and was slowly admitted into contact with the surfaces of the limestones and sea-shells. A local electric action was excited, in which the limestones and sea-shells became negative, whilst the upper stratum of sulphuret of iron was positive. The sulphate of iron and carbonate of lime suffered each a decomposition, and sulphate of lime was produced in a crystallised form upon the negative surfaces of the limestones and shells, carbonic acid gas being liberated:

moreover, this iron being deprived of its sulphuric acid, absorbed oxygen and was converted into the red oxide of iron, which was abundantly precipitated around the base of the crystals of sulphate of lime, in a powdery form.

In order to prove the correctness of this theory, on my return home I took a large basin, half filled it with pipe-clay, which I kneaded up with water to the consistence of moist putty, and embedded in the clay some pieces of limestone and some sea-shells. I next formed a stratum upon the clay of powdered sulphuret of iron, and then filled the basin with common water, and put it aside in a dark cupboard for a twelve-month. At the end of that period I brought it into the light and examined it with no small anxiety; but was delighted to find that every piece of limestone and sea-shell which had been embedded in the clay, when taken out, washed, and dried, was covered with prismatic crystals of sulphate of lime exactly similar to those found in the cliff at Weymouth but of course they were very small, though perfect. Such are the effects of LOCAL ELECTRICITY. Observe that here no battery was used, nor metal in metallic state. It was simply a close imitation of nature, but followed out only for a year; whereas nature has at her command unlimited time and resources.

Although at this time Andrew Crosse did not use the electrical network at Fyne Court anywhere near as much as in the past, he had already refined it to the extent that it could be used for medical purposes. Unfortunately, there are no specific texts or notes in existence as to how Crosse applied his electrical machine for curative purposes, and we have to rely totally on Mrs Crosse's information for an insight into this particular aspect of our story. She writes:

Mr Crosse's electrical machine was frequently in requisition for medical purposes. The poor in the neighbourhood used to go to Fyne Court to be electrified for paralysis and rheumatism, and in almost every case the effect was highly beneficial. I remember hearing of a farmer, a man upwards of sixty, who was paralysed on the left side, and had besides a distressing complaint of the salivary glands. At first, when he went to Mr Crosse, it was with difficulty that he could be assisted out of his gig; after being electrified twice a week for six weeks, he was so much better, that he could walk to Fyne Court, and the complaint in the throat was entirely removed.

The picture that suggests itself, of Crosse performing his 'electrification' of these people in his laboratory packed with wires and batteries, is just like a scene from one of the films of *Frankenstein*. It is interesting also to conclude from these remarks that there was as yet nothing like the fear of Crosse and his electrical experiments among the local population which was later to be so notable and widespread. From eagerly accepting cures at his hands, these people were shortly to denounce him as a man in league with the Devil ...

Crosse himself was undoubtedly a reasonably contented man at the time and expressed this mood in a number of poems, none of which are remarkable, but which all show a keen eye for the sights and sounds of nature. One, entitled 'Spring', reads:

> Off, cares and vexations! I'll fling ye away!
> And though ye'll come back, ye shall not come today.
> In the meads will I revel. What Fate may assign
> I toss to the winds: this day shall be mine.

These lines, like many of the others found through his sheaves of poetry, do, however, reveal his lonely and isolated life. This may have been good from the point of view of his work, but it contributed to his generally moody and introspective nature. His sole contact with the outside world — as I have already indicated — was through the medium of correspondence: when he was prepared to take time off from his experiments.

In the three years since his lecture in London, his friendship with George Singer, for instance, had been continued solely through the mails. Crosse had been constantly delighted at the increasing regard in which his friend was held, and was always interested to exchange information and opinion on scientific progress, particularly in the field of electricity.

Then, in the spring of 1817, Crosse received some shattering news. He heard that Singer had burst a blood vessel in his lungs, almost certainly from overwork. Writing to his other friend, John Kenyon, Crosse said, 'I fear his

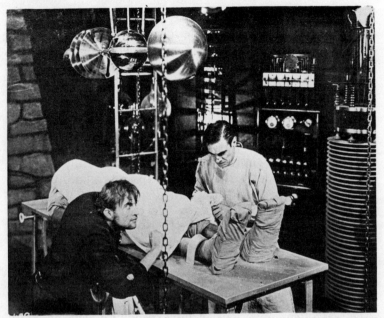

The first of the screen Frankensteins inspired by Andrew Crosse — Colin Clive about to animate his creature in the 1931 version of the story. His assistant, Fritz, is played by Dwight Frye.

mortal career must soon terminate. He is forbidden to read and scarcely to think; he who made the best use of his time of anyone I ever knew.'

Crosse's fears were well-founded: on June 28 Singer died at his mother's home in London. His overwhelming feeling of loss was again conveyed in a letter to Kenyon:

Poor Singer died yesterday. I truly lament his loss, but he died like a real philosopher. No man, whatever his rank, wealth, strength of mind and body, can say, in the vigour of his life and full enjoyment of all these blessings, I am happy. Can a person be happy who sits on the verge of a precipice? I invariably feel melancholy when I look back on past times, read past events, or examine antiquities; not from a wish of recalling such times, but from a consciousness that all belonging to myself, my family, my friends, will shortly be swept away in the same manner, and form a portion of that past which it is permitted me for a short space of time to contemplate.

93

It is clear that with Singer's death, Crosse felt he had lost the one person with whom he felt really at ease discussing his work. The one person who could follow the train of his thoughts and the direction of his experiments. From that moment, he seems to have made a conscious decision to keep the details of his scientific work to himself: he had never sought acclaim and would now merely seek to satisfy his own exacting standards and hopes.

This attitude may have been further hardened by the change in his own circumstances. His young family was now growing and needed schooling, and his wife's failing health called for frequent and expensive medication. His funds had been severely depleted by the expenditure on Fyne Court, and the returns from the land and tenants had in no way replenished these. As Cornelia Crosse has written:

> About this time the mere business affairs of life pressed heavily upon Mr Crosse: he was never a good manager, careless about money matters, and, though not in the least extravagant, he was often injudicious in his expenditure. The necessary expenses of a large family, alterations in the house and grounds, rebuilding of farm premises, and those many drawbacks of landed property, all contributed to cripple his resources. As Mr Crosse himself often observed, 'My family were learned and honourable men as long as I can look back; but they had the happy knack of turning a guinea into a shilling, and I have inherited the faculty pretty strongly'.

His gloomy thoughts translated themselves into more lines of poetry which he scrawled out on scraps of paper in a peculiar, almost illegible hand. In one, entitled, 'Love and Hate', he wrote:

> Then will he hate; and every vein
> Where love once held her throne
> Will wake to never-dying pain,
> To a hell before unknown.

In another, to mark the New Year, he is equally joyless as he complains against the bells heralding the first day of January:

Would ye disturb the silent crowds
  Whose dust forgotten sleeps below,
And wrench them from their mouldering shrouds
  For this sad world of sin and woe?

Again to rouse the victor's ire,
  To wrap new towns in sheets of flame,
Again command the poet's lyre
  To hymn those deeds of blood and shame?

Would ye call back to mortal strife
  The maniac's scream, the felon's gloom,
The unutterable woes of life,
  Again to sink into the tomb?

For a time, Crosse seems to have thought seriously about entering the Church and taking Holy orders. 'But I fear I am utterly unworthy of taking upon me so sacred a function,' he confided to John Kenyon, whose letters at this time seem devoted to trying to raise his spirits. The general state of his mind was also revealed in another letter to Kenyon when Crosse wrote, 'I sometimes, as if to punish myself, indulge in painfully interesting recollections, and love, like the madman who scooped out his eye with a bone, to tear my heartstrings in keenly calling to mind days which can never return.'

On a brief excursion outside Broomfield, when he went to see a relative sailing from Plymouth to India, he had an extraordinary experience which again showed his troubled state. Cornelia Crosse found details of this scribbled on a piece of paper, and her account is as follows:

Mr Crosse had come back as far as Exeter, where he slept. He was very much fatigued, and felt low. He described that he had scarcely lain down upon his bed, when a sudden train of thought burst upon him with such intensity that it seemed almost like inspiration: he was not asleep, it was no dream; but yet in imagination he roamed over the universe; and beheld with the eye of fancy the unbounded glories of creation; it appeared to him, he said, as if the soul had quitted its prison of clay, and was free to reach the limits of space, or rather to annihilate space with the intensity of its perception. Centuries of time were condensed in those moments of ecstatic life, and Nature's laws seemed clear to the omniscience of its glance: a sense of blessedness sustained him — he felt immortal.

'So thought I, in the dead of silent night,
Till, neith the flow of imagery tired,
I sank resistless in the arms of sleep.'

Mrs Crosse adds a rider to this description of her husband's experience: 'Thus ends the poetical description of his reverie, which reminds one of what Sir Humphrey Davy describes that he felt while under the influence of nitrous oxide gas.'

Crosse's thoughts on death also prompted him to begin writing a story about a place where death was unknown — where, instead of dying, people and things merely diminished. This extraordinary fantasy, 'The Island of Elattosis', seems to have possessed him for a short time, but unfortunately he did not complete it because, as he later told his wife, 'I found out how impossible it is to represent anything contrary to nature.' For my part, I think this story has certain elements which allow it to be classified as a work of Science Fiction, and because of the ever-growing interest in this literary genre, I have reprinted the story — incomplete as it is, yet just as Crosse left it — in the Appendix to this book.

As the pressures seemed to mount around him, and Crosse found it increasingly difficult to sleep at night, he took to going on long rambles over the neighbouring countryside. The stillness and darkness seemed to relax him, as did the wild life he came across. In an essay he published later in his life entitled, 'Walks on the Quantock Hills', he wrote:

In my walks on the Quantocks I often reflected how little we know of the habitudes of animals. How strong are their affections, how powerful their instincts — almost approaching to the confines of reason. When this great tyrant man is asleep, little dreaming of their gambols, then they quit their hiding-places, and revel in comparative security. Often have I stumbled on the red deer, while crossing the hills in the dead of night, or disturbed the fox with the light of my lantern. I never found any animal, except occasionally my own species, whom I could not tame by persevering kindness.

Many strange adventures with bird and beast have occurred to me in these rambles, and once I nearly lost my life from a tremendous storm that overtook me at night; but I have been well repaid for all minor inconveniences by the opportunities afforded me of observing the phenomena of Nature. The startling meteor, the magnificent aurora borealis, the lunar rainbow spanning the horizon, with pale and mystical light, and, far above all, the refulgent planets rolling in their appointed course, and at a vastly greater distance, the ocean of starry worlds, whose size and numbers mock the telescopic calculations of erring philosophers.

The 'tremendous storm' that Crosse mentioned was to have a profound effect upon him. For as he struggled home through the lashing rain, clambering dangerously on the slopes of the Quantocks and nearly slipping to his death, he had the transitory nature of life brought dramatically home to him. Then as lightning cracked over his head and thunder rolled all around him, he vowed that if he got back safely to Fyne Court he would change his ways. It seemed to him, too, that the electrical display was a kind of omen. Perhaps, by being bolder in his work, he would overcome his depression and at the same time give himself the mental alertness to tackle his domestic problems.

If he wanted confirmation of his conviction he did not have to wait long. Once again it was underlined by a narrow escape from death — perhaps even narrower than on the Quantock hillside. I quote from Mrs Crosse's *Memoirs*:

Mr Crosse was returning home one day by the side of one of the ponds in the grounds of Fyne Court, when he saw a cat sitting by the water. In a spirit of mischief he sprang forward to catch the animal, with the intention of throwing her into the water, but, to use his own words, 'She was too quick for me to catch her, but not quick enough to escape me altogether. I held her for an instant, and she turned and bit me severely on the hand. I threw her from me, and in doing so, I saw that her hair was stivered; the cat was evidently ill. She died the same day of hydrophobia! The circumstance passed from my memory as

97

weeks rolled on; but about three months afterwards, I felt one morning a great pain in my arm; at the same time feeling exceedingly thirsty, I called for a glass of water: at the instant that I was about to raise the tumbler to my lips, a strong spasm shot across my throat; immediately the terrible conviction came to my mind that I was about to fall a victim to hydrophobia, the consequence of the bite that I had received from the cat!

'The agony of mind I endured for one hour is indescribable: the contemplation of such a horrible death — death from hydrophobia — was almost insupportable; the torments of hell itself could not have surpassed what I suffered. The pain, which had first commenced in my hand, passed up to the elbow, and from thence to the shoulder, threatening to extend. I felt all human aid was useless, and I believed that I must die.

'At length, I began to reflect upon my condition, I said to myself, either I shall die, or I shall not; if I do, it will only be a similar fate which many have suffered, and many more must suffer, and I must bear it like a man: if, on the other hand, there is any hope of my life, my only chance is in summoning my utmost resolution, defying the attack, and exerting every effort of my mind. Accordingly, feeling that physical as well as mental exertion was necessary, I took my gun, shouldered it, and went out for the purpose of shooting, my arm aching the while intolerably.

'I met with no sport, but I walked the whole afternoon, exerting, at every step I went, a strong mental effort against the disease: when I returned to the house, I was decidedly better; I was able to eat some dinner and drank water as usual. The next morning the aching pain had gone down to my elbow, the following it went down to the wrist, and the third day left me altogether. I mentioned the circumstance to Dr Kinglake, and he said, he certainly considered that I had had an attack of hydrophobia, which would possibly have proved fatal had I not struggled against it by a strong effort of mind.'

Now completely resolved, Crosse threw himself into the business of running his estate and extending the range of his experiments. The bad winter of 1821 which had passed turned into a glorious spring and hot summer, and soon the land was rich with grazing cattle and lying lush with a full, ripening harvest. In his laboratory, Crosse busied himself with his electrical equipment and his most ambitious

A film set that might literally have been based on Andrew Crosse's laboratory: Peter Cushing as Frankenstein in The Evil of Frankenstein *(1964).*

project yet — a huge voltaic battery three times bigger than anything he had constructed previously.

A few months later he wrote to the ever-solicitous John Kenyon:

> I have lately constructed a voltaic battery of ONE THOUSAND AND TWENTY-FIVE pairs of metallic plates; also an electrical battery, composed of talc plates coated with tin-foil. This last battery being interposed between the poles of the voltaic battery, charged with common pump-water becomes *instantly* charged, and to an intensity sufficient to deflagrate metallic leaves, explode fulminating powders, cause iron wire to perpetually scintillate, &c. &c. I have hopes to be enabled thus to form an apparatus capable of giving perpetual LIGHT, HEAT, and MOTION. I have likewise made some very interesting discoveries in electrical crystallisation, having produced cubes of metallic silver, and four-sided prisms capped with four-sided pyramids of muriate of mercury, from their respective solutions, by means of slow electric action.

Such was the improvement in his health, that Andrew

Crosse even began accepting public invitations. In January 1822, he attended a special meeting in nearby Taunton which sent a petition to Parliament appealing for a relief in the oppressive taxation which those present said 'has swallowed up the capital of the farmer, and brought the greater proportion of independent yeomen to the brink of ruin'. Unless something was speedily done about this, they said, 'it must terminate in the annihilation of that most excellent and invaluable body of men'. Crosse added his own weight to the petition with a brief speech in which he said, 'Within a few years the taxes have been quadrupled, and three-fourths of them must be taken off before their pressure will cease to be intolerable.' He believed a complete change of government and new system of taxation was essential for this to happen.

Crosse also took part in local politics — though he had no particular affiliation to any party — lending assistance to the campaign of one of his neighbours, Charles Tynte of Halswell Park, for a seat in Government. However, he was an unpredictable man in this, as in the rest of his life. He was horrified, for instance, when he suggested that one candidate should make a toast to another at a dinner for some act of public kindness and was told, 'Better not, better not; it won't do.' On another occasion, he actually spoke from a platform and was greeted with cries that he was like Oliver Cromwell. Sharply he turned on his hecklers and retorted, 'Gentlemen, I thank you for the compliment. If I were Oliver Cromwell I would sweep all such as you from the face of the earth.' At the end of the meeting, a member of the audience approached him and said, 'Why, Crosse, you don't care for the whole world' — and he snapped back, 'Not if I think they're wrong and I am right.' Despite his efforts — or perhaps because of them — Tynte was beaten at the polls, and Crosse complained bitterly about this in a letter to Kenyon: 'We're beat, almost dead beat. Money, cursed bribery, and intimidation of tenants, have beat us, added to our too great confidence and damned mismanagement ... A bigoted, narrow-souled Oxonio-Devonian, or Devilian, is at the head of the poll.'

Such diversions apart, it was his work which really

absorbed Crosse at this time. In particular, he was tackling
the problem of thunder clouds and their composition by
making extensive use of his network of copper wires and
batteries. For many long days and nights he worked with
this equipment, drawing down electric current from the
skies and trying to assess what he learned. Flashes of light
often danced along the wires around Fyne Court, loud
reports were heard from inside his laboratory, and a white
glow suffused the windows of the 'electrical room'.
Although he could not know it, the superstitious local folk
had seen many of these strange displays and were beginning
to mutter dark things about the Master of Fyne Court.

Crosse, though, was deep in his own deliberations, as
Cornelia Crosse tells us: 'He thought long and hard on the
subject, but no suggestion came. At length, one morning,
while he was shaving, the explanation suddenly darted into
his mind, and, with a schoolboy's glee, he shouted,
"Eureka!" and rushing down to his electrical room, with
the lather on his chin, he immediately sought to test his
theory by experiment. He was right; he *had* "found it".'

Some years later, when he had refined his conclusions,
Crosse wrote this simplified explanation of what he had
discovered:

It is known to Electricians, that if an insulated plate, composed
of a perfect or an imperfect conductor, be electrified, the
Electricity communicated will radiate from the centre to the
circumference, *increasing* in force as the squares of the distances
from the centre; whereas, in a thunder-cloud the reverse takes
place, as its power *diminishes* from the centre to the
circumference. First a nucleus appears to be formed, say of
positive Electricity, embracing a large portion of the centre of
the cloud, round which is a negative zone of equal power with
the former; then follow the other zones in pairs, diminishing in
power to the edge of the cloud. *Directly below this cloud*, according
to the laws of inductive Electricity must exist, on the surface of
the earth, a nucleus of opposite corresponding zone of positive,
and with other zones of electrified surface, corresponding in
number to those of the cloud above, although each is oppositely
electrified. A discharge of the positive nucleus above into that of
the negative below, is commonly that which occurs when a
flash of lightning is seen; or from the positive below to the

negative above, as the case may be: and this discharge may take place, according to the laws of Electricity, through any or all of the surrounding zones *without influencing their respective electricities* otherwise than by weakening their force, by the removal of a portion of the electric fluid from the central nucleus above to that below: every successive flash from the cloud to the earth, or from the earth to the cloud, weakening the charge of the plate of air, of which the cloud and the earth form the two opposite coatings. Much might be said upon this head, of which the above is but a slight sketch.

However, Crosse was not a man to rest on such triumphs. Another letter from his papers of this period, addressed to an unknown correspondent, gives us a clear picture of what his life at Broomfield must have been like through the whole decade.

Broomfield, May 4th, 1832.

My dear sir,

I received your letter the day before yesterday. The kindness of it I shall never forget. I am in the midst of all sorts of business, — selling hay, barking oak, cutting down poles, gardening, &c. &c. Far above all, I am working like a slave in my laboratory, and have two fires *constantly* burning night and day. I have formed crystals on several new plans, and I am preparing a very extensive apparatus. I wish my means were half as ample and extensive as the apparatus I would fain construct! I do not go to London to see the gewgaws and frippery and childish nonsense of the coronation. How much mankind have to learn before they begin to be ashamed of such trash!

I have just put together a water battery of sixty-three large zinc and copper cylinders, each cylinder equal to a nine-inch square plate. It gives a small but intense constant stream of light, between two charcoal points the heat of which will fire gun-powder. I am about to increase it to 100 pairs.

Five thousand of such cylinders as these would make a glorious exhibition, but they would cost £500. Each pair of cylinders is contained in a glass jar, which holds about three pints. The shock through the thin part of the skin, even quite dry, is almost intolerable. It is my belief that 1,000 of such cylinders, or even less, would produce potassium from alkali. I

am half stewed with the heat of my furnaces, which I am
obliged to watch closely.

Yours truly,
ANDREW CROSSE.

Although, of course, Crosse had not lectured on his work
in public since 1814, it was becoming more widely known in
scientific circles, primarily through Singer's book and the
reports which filtered out from Broomfield. He was also
showing himself prepared to receive visitors who came to
his door with a serious interest in what he was trying to do.

Accounts of the electrician at this time describe him as
being a slightly stooping figure with a long, thin face,
melancholy eyes and brown hair greying at the edges. He
invariably wore a velvet jacket as his 'laboratory costume'.

Some of his visitors were clearly in awe of him, and one,
Edward W. Cox, who visited him in the early 1830s and
wrote an account for the *Taunton Courier*, believed him to be
a genius:

> The presence of genius you discover in Andrew Crosse before
> you have conversed with him for a quarter of an hour. The talk
> of most men, even those who are reputed as wise or witty, is
> merely repetition of that which you have heard, in substance if
> not in form, from other men fifty times before, and read as
> often. But Mr Crosse's talk is his own. You may differ from his
> opinions, you may question his accuracy, you may contest his
> arguments, you may smile sometimes at views that seem to you
> visionary and wild, because they are different from your own
> habitual trains of thinking, and therefore startle you; but you
> cannot complain that they are commonplace; they are not
> echoes of the voices of others, nor gems in a new setting — *alter
> et idem* — stolen from books old or new.

Such visitors would be given a conducted tour of Crosse's
laboratory, an explanation of his work and, if the weather
was suitable, a demonstration of the working of his
electrical network and batteries. He proved himself an
accomplished and open-minded instructor, ready with a
sharp wit when taken to task over any particular element of
his work.

On one occasion, Cornelia Crosse tells us, he was exhibiting two enormous Leyden jars used for charging with electricity by the conducting wires, when an elderly visitor looked at him with a very serious expression and demanded, 'Mr Crosse, don't you think it is rather impious to bottle the lightning?' Immediately the electrician shot back the reply, 'Let me answer your question by asking another. Don't you think, sir, it might be considered rather impious to bottle the rain water?'

The people of Broomfield, not to mention the servants at Fyne Court, were just as intrigued by what Crosse was doing as the men of science. The servants, for their part, were under strict instructions not to enter the laboratory except when specifically invited by their master. Cornelia Crosse tells us of a young housemaid who was apparently unable to contain her curiosity about what went on in the 'electrical room' and slipped in one day when Crosse was out, ostensibly to do some dusting. Tempted by the array of scientific equipment, she could not resist touching the brass cylinder marked '*Noli me tangere*'.

'There was a considerable amount of electricity present in the atmosphere,' says Mrs Crosse, 'and she got a rather severe shock. She forthwith went to her master, and complained that the "nasty thing" in the gallery nearly knocked her down. "I thought that I told you never to touch the apparatus," said Mr Crosse. "Yes, sir; but I thought you had written 'No Danger' on it!" If all bad translators were so corrected, it would save the world a great deal of literary trash!'

The local farm labourers and people of the district were becoming increasingly suspicious and even afraid of Andrew Crosse's experiments. To them, his dabbling with the elements of the storm was tampering with the works of God, and the displays of flashing lights seen above and around Fyne Court made him the subject of endless gossip and rumour.

When Crosse went walking or rode out on his horse across the Quantocks, he could not help sensing that people were somehow avoiding him. They were showing the usual deference to the squire, certainly, but with a hint of fear in their manner, too. It was probably some little time before he actually overheard what was being said about him: and then quite by chance on a still day, the air carried the words of one yokel to another as he passed by:

'Don't you know him? That's Crosse of Broomfield — the thunder and lightning man. You can't go near his cursed house at night without danger of your life. Them as have been there have seen devils, all surrounded by lightning, dancing on the wires that he has put up round his grounds.'

Thus Crosse earned his nickname, 'The Thunder and Lightning Man', and it is one that stuck to him throughout his life and has been remembered in this area of the Quantocks right through to the present day.

However, if those who did not understand what he was doing were coming to fear him, there were others who wished to honour him. In 1827 he was delighted to receive a visit from the great pioneer of electro-chemistry, Sir Humphrey Davy, now an ageing but much respected and admired man whose invention of the miner's safety lamp a few years earlier had carried his name around the world. In the autumn of that year he had been staying at the little Quantock village of Stowey, and requested the opportunity of visiting Crosse whose work he had read about.

The electrician later recalled that although Davy was weakened by the disease which was soon to end his life (he died in 1829), he was driven over to Fyne Court by a mutual acquaintance. Crosse then conducted the venerable president of the Royal Society over his home, and finally, into the laboratory.

'Never shall I forget,' he wrote, 'seeing Davy's fine melancholy eyes brighten up, as he looked at the furnaces. For a few moments he seemed himself again, the languor of disease had fled, and his old activity was expressed in every look and action.'

The kindly interest which his fellow scientists and electricians were showing towards his work, undoubtedly provided Crosse with some satisfaction and encouragement. He worked on with a will in his laboratory, confident that he could prove some of the extraordinary and revolutionary ideas for the use of electricity that were forming in his mind.

He had no way of knowing that other storm clouds, far darker and more menacing than those which he used for his experiments, were beginning to gather on his horizon. Nor that he was soon to become involved in a discovery which was to make him infamous and attach his name to one of the most bizarre mysteries in the annals of science.

8

The Creation of Life

The atmosphere of suspicion which was beginning to surround Crosse and his work — it was outright fear in some quarters — developed at a pace in the middle 1830s. In local gossip it was said the Master of Fyne Court was practising the Black Arts, challenging the powers of the Almighty, and even adversely affecting local agriculture as a result of his experiments: a poor harvest and a potato blight were both attributed to his agency.

Visitors to Fyne Court who inquired in Taunton or Bridgwater which was the way to Crosse's isolated home were met with either reluctantly imparted information, a sullen silence or outright hostility. In her book, *Quantock Country* (1952), Berta Lawrence describes one such instance which will suffice for several similar occasions when the attitudes were exactly the same:

> On one occasion a number of distinguished men, including the Dean of Westminster and Baron Liebig, asked in Bridgwater how they should reach Squire Crosse's. The innkeeper from whom they tried to hire a carriage reported them to the police, for (a) they were speaking a foreign tongue (actually they were discussing in German the cheese-making at Cheddar which they had just visited). (b) They might be Chartists or revolutionaries. (c) They were friends of Squire Crosse, known to many as the Wizard of Broomfield, suspected of practising

black arts, and accused by farmers of causing storms by his cursed electrical experiments. Further, in politics he held advanced liberal principles and had republican sympathies towards the French Revolution.

Despite such attitudes, Crosse was not to be deflected from his purpose, and chose to ignore all the gossip as if it did not exist. Indeed, in 1836 he rather surprisingly agreed to attend the annual meeting of the British Association for the Advancement of Science being held at Bristol. It was surprising because he had never associated himself with any scientific bodies, and even more so because he was not sure the gathering would even understand what he was trying to achieve. In fact, he confided later, 'I was very uncertain about going, for I always shrank from pushing myself forward, and I was but little in spirits for such an occasion, for a constant succession of family illnesses had crushed me almost to the earth.'

None the less, he allowed himself to be persuaded and travelled from Broomfield to Bristol. It was a decision he was later to have cause to bitterly regret.

Initially, however, his appearance and lecture seemed an unqualified success. As Mrs Crosse wrote in her *Memoirs*: 'The enthusiasm with which Mr Crosse's discoveries were received is almost beyond credence. The impression is vividly remembered even now, after a lapse of twenty years. When the circumstance is recurred to, persons, otherwise strangers, have described to me, in glowing language, the effect of words so simple, yet so earnest, which characterised Mr Crosse's utterance of the results he had met with in searching into Nature's laws; the order of his inquiries was at once profound and original.' Among the British Association's papers is the following brief report of Crosse's speech.

Mr Crosse described to the meeting, that by an arrangement in which he passed a voltaic current, excited by water alone, through certain mineral solutions, he had formed various crystalline bodies analogous to those found in nature. In these experiments, in which he used long-continued voltaic action of low intensity, he had obtained artificial crystals of quartz, arragonite, carbonates of lime, lead, and copper, besides more than twenty other artificial minerals. 'One regularly shaped crystal of quartz, measuring $^3/_{16}$ of an inch in length, and $^1/_{16}$ of an inch in diameter, and readily scratching glass, was formed from fluo-silicic acid exposed to the electric action of a water battery from the 8th of March to the latter end of June, 1836.' Mr Crosse added, in conclusion, that he was fully convinced that it was possible even to make diamonds, and that at no distant period every kind of mineral would be formed by the ingenuity of man. 'If,' said he, 'any members of the Association would favour me with a visit at my house, they shall be received with hospitality, though in a wild and savage region on the Quantock Hills, and I shall be proud to repeat my experiment in their presence.' Mr Crosse sat down amidst long continued cheering.

The report added that the Chairman of the meeting, Professor Adam Sedgwick, one of the leading geologists of the day, in thanking the speaker said that 'Mr Crosse may have hitherto concealed himself, but from this time forth he must stand before the world as public property.' They were to prove strangely prophetic words — but not quite in the manner the Professor had intended.

Records indicate that Crosse also delivered two other speeches to the assembly, 'Some Improvements on the Voltaic Battery' and 'Observations on Atmospheric Electricity'. Again both were improvised as he had prepared no notes, and unfortunately there are no existing records of either speech.

Crosse did not wait to receive the further praise which the members wished to shower upon him. 'I slipped away out of it all,' he remarked later, and two or three days before the gathering had actually closed, was back in the familiar surroundings of Broomfield, hard at work.

John Kenyon, his long-time correspondent, heard of his triumph at Bristol and wrote saying he was sorry he had not been there. He had been told that Crosse had 'modestly retreated from being one of the great show-beasts of the meeting', and went on, 'How could we have believed, forty years ago at Seyers, conjuror as we called you, that you should be writing with crystal pens of your own making [referring to the electrical crystals of quartz which scratched glass], and I be carrying your autographs about the country.' He concluded, 'Well, it has pleased God to try you with much household distress for some years ... and now, after all your furnace-watchings and explosions, whether vinous or electrical, comes at last a deserved reputation in part payment.'

However, not everyone had been impressed or convinced by what Crosse had said. Cornelia Crosse tells us the euphoria of the meeting quickly evaporated. 'It is quite curious to observe the amount of ignorant and absurd abuse that was later showered upon Mr Crosse from some quarters. To jealousy and prejudice may be ascribed much of the calumny of mankind: if there is one class of community who enthusiastically accept a new truth, there are always a number of oppositionists who seek to pull down the idol that their fellows have raised.'

Crosse appears to have treated most of these attacks with 'the silent contempt they deserved', but one particularly virulent attack on him in the columns of the *Bristol Atlas* by a Dr Ritchie, who had also attended the meeting, finally stirred him to defend himself.

He prefaced his remarks with the statement that it was 'exceedingly disagreeable' for him to have to write, but as he 'detested nothing so much as cant or humbug of any sort', he felt compelled to reply to such an unfair attack as that of Dr Ritchie. He went on to describe how he had been pressed to address the Bristol meeting and that he 'never attached the least merit to what I had done, nor tacked the word discovery to any of my experiments, but gave a simple statement of what took place.' The letter continued:

A great many mistakes and exaggerations concerning me have been circulated in different papers at different times; but it is no fault of mine that such things occurred. In fact, it cannot be expected that those who have not made a particular science their study should be correct in their details concerning such science. It is very true that, in my electrical room, a brass ball connected with an atmospherical conductor is suspended over a battery, so arranged as to be united or disunited at pleasure; but such battery is a *common electrical*, and most assuredly *not a voltaic one.* Dr Ritchie must have known well that the absurd report of having brought into my house streams of lightning as large as the mast of a ship originated in a joke that fell from the eloquent lips of a distinguished professor who attended the meeting. Dr Ritchie, however, in supposing such a miracle possible, compares the *inferiority* of such an enormous electrical current with the *superiority* of that manifested by Richman and Romas, the former of whom was killed by want of proper precaution, having contrived an apparatus to bring the electric fluid into his house, but apparently without making a due arrangement to carry it out. The latter, by means of a kite, elevated far above the highest of my poles, brought down an amazing quantity of electricity; but such a temporary apparatus as a kite is ill-calculated for scientific purposes, to say nothing of the extreme danger attending it. I have really no wish to be knocked on the head in aspiring to eclipse my neighbours ...

He next insinuates that I claim as a discovery the filling of battery cells with water instead of dilute acid. When did I state this? I may, however, in justice to myself observe, that I have not heard of effects produced by other batteries filled with common water at all equal to what are produced by the arrangements I adopt, and for the truth of this I appeal to those scientific men who have witnessed their effects. Dr R then notices my remark on the greater power of these batteries between the hours of *seven and ten* in the morning, and that such increase of strength was unconnected with any meter whatever. Here he observes that I do not know the properties of the agents used in a voltaic battery, and proceeds to lecture me on the alteration of the conducting power of primary and secondary conductors by the influence of heat, summing up with the inference that the increase of temperature is the cause of the increase of power observed, and that, too, between the hours of seven and ten in the morning! I shall only say, in reply to this, that my batteries are placed in a room with a south aspect, and that every fair day the sun shines full upon them, at which time the shock they give to the human body is *decidedly less* than at the hours alluded to. As to my ignorance of the effects of heat, &c., on voltaic batteries, I have tried fluids of all temperatures, and often used boiling water in the cells, which occasions a considerable increase of power.

To say the truth, I have made a much greater number of experiments in this branch of the science than Dr R may be aware of, but am not about to enter at present upon the comparative powers of the simple electric, the decomposing, the fusing, or the magnetic effects produced from differently formed batteries. *Opinion to me is but a wind, experiment a rock.* Now comes his attack on my electrical crystallisations of substances. I before stated all I knew concerning M Becquerel. Had M Becquerel been the Englishman and I the foreigner, I do believe that gentleman would have received from Dr R the censure instead of myself, *as if it were a crime for a countryman hitherto unknown to experimentalise at all.* The next remark on me is: 'According to Mr Crosse, either pole of the battery will crystallise equally well.' When and where did I state this absurdity? It is the first time that I have heard of it. I have, however, met with some curious and quite unexpected facts which bear on this part of the subject, which neither chemist nor electrician would have expected without previous trial. Then follows: 'The crystallisation of quartz and carbon is still doubtful.' That I have produced the first by the electric action long continued, as also arragonite, I can prove by unimpeachable witnesses; the last (carbon) I have not attempted. As I never aimed at procuring public applause (although I am deeply sensible of the great kindness I have received from my friends and the public) but I have pursued science for its own sake, those shafts of Dr Ritchie fall powerless against me. I cannot, however, refrain from adding that I would scorn to admit for one instant such a spirit towards another as he has evinced towards me, a stranger to him in all respects, save public report, even for the power of crystallising carbon.

Crosse clearly found the whole argument distasteful, and added as a footnote to the Editor that he had been delayed in sending his reply because of illness, and that he was anxious in future 'to decline engaging in scientific warfare with any one, having neither inclination nor time for that kind of amusement.'

It was to prove a vain hope.

The dust had scarcely settled on this controversy when, in 1837, just after Crosse had celebrated his fifty-third birthday, the event occurred which has puzzled scientists to this very day. It all began normally enough as just another of his experiments on electro-crystallisation. But what occurred during the succeeding weeks was far from ordinary: in fact it was completely unique, resulting in the astonishing creation of tiny, living insects from stone. Crosse, to all intents and purposes, had discovered the mystery of existence — he had created life!

I do not believe any modern re-telling of this amazing sequence of events could possibly be as convincing as Crosse's own report, actually written down as the experiment proceeded, and so it is his words which follow.

In the course of my endeavours to form artificial minerals by a long continued electric action on fluids holding in solution such substances as were necessary to my purpose, I had recourse to every variety of contrivance that I could think of; amongst others I constructed a wooden frame, which supported a Wedgewood funnel, within which rested a quart basin on a circular piece of mahogany. [Illustration overleaf.] When this basin was filled with a fluid, a strip of flannel wetted with the same was suspended over the side of the basin and inside the funnel, which, acting as a syphon, conveyed the fluid out of the basin through the funnel in successive drops: these drops fell into a smaller funnel of glass placed beneath the other, and which contained a piece of somewhat porous red oxide of iron from Vesuvius. This stone was kept constantly electrified by means of two platina wires on each side of it, connected with the poles of a voltaic battery of ten pairs of five-inch zinc and copper plates. The droppings of the second funnel fell into a wide-mouthed bottle; and they were poured back again into the basin, when the vessel was getting empty. It must not be supposed that the stone from Vesuvius was in any way connected with the result of the experiment. It had been selected for its porosity. The fluid with which the basin was filled was made as follows: A piece of black flint, which had been exposed to a red heat, was reduced to powder. Of this powder two ounces were taken, and mixed intimately with six ounces of carbonate of potassa, and then exposed to a strong heat for fifteen minutes. The fused compound was then poured into a black lead crucible in an air furnace; it was reduced to powder while still warm; boiling water was poured on it, and it was kept boiling for some minutes. The greater part of the soluble glass thus formed was taken up by the water. To a portion of the silicate of potassa thus formed I added some boiling water to dilute it, and then slowly added hydrocholoric acid to supersaturation.

The object of subjecting this fluid to a long continued electric

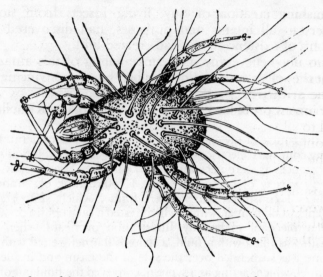

A sketch of one of the extraordinary insects which came to life in Andrew Crosse's laboratory, the Acari Crossii.

action through the intervention of a porous stone was to form if possible crystals of silica; but this failed. On the fourteenth day from the commencement of this experiment I observed through a lens a few small whitish excrescences or nipples, projecting from about the middle of the electrified stone. On the eighteenth day these projections enlarged, and struck out seven or eight filaments, each of them longer than the hemisphere on which they grew. On the twenty-sixth day these appearances assumed the form of a *perfect insect*, standing erect on a few bristles which formed its tail. Till this period I had no notion that these appearances were other than an incipient mineral formation. On the twenty-eighth day these little creatures moved their legs. I must now say that I was not a little astonished. After a few days they detached themselves from the stone, and moved about at pleasure. [See sketch.]

In the course of a few weeks about a hundred of them made their appearance on the stone. I examined them with a microscope, and observed that the smaller ones appeared to have only six legs, the larger ones eight. These insects are pronounced to be of the genus *acarus*; but there appears to be a difference of opinion as to whether they are a known species; some assert that they are not.

114

To say that Crosse was dumbfounded would be an understatement: and it was only his training as a scientist and his natural modesty that prevented him making any claims about his 'creatures'. For a start, he was not sure what they were, so he told no one about what had occurred in the privacy of his laboratory, and racked his brains as to how insects could have emerged under conditions normally fatal to all forms of life, in a highly caustic solution and out of contact with the air.

The simplest answer that occurred to him was that they had arisen from ova deposited by insects flying in the atmosphere and then hatched by the electric action. However, he found it impossible to believe that an ovum could shoot out filaments as these creatures had done, or that these filaments could become bristles. When he

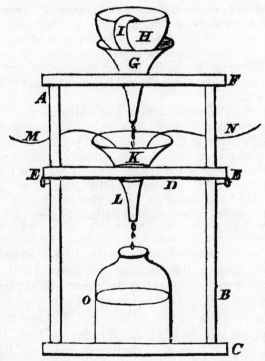

The equipment used by Andrew Crosse in the amazing experiment of the insects.

115

examined the equipment again to see if there was any likelihood of this being true, he could not find the slightest remains of any shells from which the insects might have hatched.

The more Crosse pondered, the harder he found it to believe that the electric action alone had brought the insects to life. Then, when he wondered if perhaps they had been generated from the water in the vessels, he again made another close inspection of all his equipment. Not a trace of any insect could be found. There seemed to be only one course of action now open to him: he must try the experiment once more to see if it had been just a freak. Again we have his report of what happened:

> I used a battery of twelve pairs, between the poles of which were interposed a series of seven glass cylinders, filled with the following concentrated solutions: 1. Nitrate of copper. 2. Carbonate of potassa. 3. Sulphate of copper. 4. Green sulphate of iron. 5. Sulphate of zinc. 6. Water acidified with a minute portion of hydrochloric acid. 7. Water poured on powdered arsenic. All these cylinders were connected with the positive pole, and were electrically united together by arcs of sheet copper, so that the same electrical current passed through the whole of them.
>
> After many months' action and consequent formation of certain crystalline matters, I observed similar excrescences with those before described at the edge of the fluid in every one of the cylinders except two which contained the carbonate of potassa and the metallic arsenic; and in due time the whitish appearances were developed into insects. In my first experiment I had made use of flannel, wood, and a volcanic stone. In the last, none of these substances were present.

As the weeks dragged into months, Crosse found he was no nearer solving this strange problem. He had even dismissed a lingering idea that the electric fluid might have animated the remains of insects or fossil eggs previously existing in the stone or silica. He wrote, 'In some cases these insects appear two inches *under* the electric fluid, but after emerging from it they were destroyed if thrown back.'

Undeterred, he felt he had no alternative but to go back

to the laboratory and try the experiment yet again, making absolutely sure that he was allowing no extraneous matter whatsoever into the equipment which might produce the insects. I quote from his report:

I calcined black gun-flints in a crucible, and flung them while hot into water; I then dried and reduced them to powder. Of this powder I mixed one ounce, and intimately mixed it with three ounces of carbonate of potassa. I fused them together for five hours, increasing the heat, until it exceeded that necessary to melt cast iron. I removed the crucible, and then allowed the contents to become solid, which formed into a pale green glass. While still *hot*, I broke them into pieces: these *hot* pieces I threw into a vessel of boiling distilled water, I had previously prepared an apparatus to act electrically upon this fluid. It consisted of a common tubulated glass retort. The beak of the retort rested in a cup of pure mercury, from which proceeded a platinum wire, which passed up through the whole length of the retort, and when it reached the bulb was bent at right angles, so as nearly to touch the bottom of the bulb. The glass tube, which fitted air-tight into the neck of this retort, had a platinum wire passed straight through it, the upper part of which was hermetically sealed into the upper part of the tube, and the lower part of the wire was continued downwards. The two platinum wires were at a distance of about two inches from each other.

When all was ready I poured the solution still *hot* into the bulb of the retort, thus affording a conducting medium between the two platinum wires, connected with the opposite poles of a small voltaic battery. An electric action commenced; oxygen and hydrogen gases were liberated; the volume of atmospheric air was soon expelled. Every care had been taken to avoid atmospheric contact and admittance of extraneous matter, and the retort itself had been previously washed with hot alcohol. This apparatus was placed in a dark cellar. I discovered no sign of incipient animal formation until on the 140th day, when I plainly distinguished *one* acurus actively crawling about *within* the bulb of the retort. I found that I had made a great error in this experiment; and I believe it was in consequence of this error that I not only lost sight of the single insect, but never saw any others in this apparatus. I had omitted to insert within the bulb of the retort a *resting place* for these acari (they are always destroyed if they fall back into the fluid from which they have emerged). It is strange that, in a solution *eminently caustic* and

117

under an atmosphere of oxihydrogen gas, one single acarus should have made its appearance.

Crosse now felt he had to accept the fact that he *had* created a life form from inanimate objects. He *had* achieved what no man, scientist or layman, had done before — though millions had dreamed of it and thousands had tried to achieve it. The evidence wriggled and crawled before his very eyes in the laboratory of his country mansion. He was even more startled to note that 'when a number of these insects, in perfect state, congregate, ova are the result.' They not only were alive, they could reproduce, too!

However, another more terrible thought now occurred to him. Should he tell anyone? And if he did — would anyone believe such an incredible story when he hardly dared believe it himself?

Crosse's dilemma resolved itself in a most unexpected way. For while he was out walking over his beloved Quantocks, who should he meet but a man who had previously visited Fyne Court and proved himself sympathetic to scientific endeavours, the poet Robert Southey. In the light of what we have learned about Southey's part in the creation of *Frankenstein*, it was a strange quirk of fate that should cause *him* to be the first to hear how Crosse had achieved in *fact* what Mary Shelley's hero had striven to do in fiction: animate the inanimate.

Crosse was deep in thought, his eyes fixed to the ground, and pondering the strange development, when he was suddenly conscious of a carriage toiling up the hill in the direction of Stowey. Walking behind the carriage was its passenger who he quickly recognised as Southey. The smile of greeting and request after his health convinced Crosse immediately that here was the serious-minded soul to whom he could unburden himself.

A moment more and the electrician began pouring out the details of what had happened in his laboratory to the incredulous poet. All thoughts of his journey fled from Southey's mind and he called for the carriage to halt while he sat down to listen to Crosse's discovery. He had come to the Quantocks to improve his health, and revisit some of the scenes that had so delighted him in earlier years. Now he had run into one of the strangest stories he had ever heard, and as he was later to comment: 'I am the first traveller who has ever been stopped by so extraordinary an announcement.'

When Crosse had finished his description, Southey admitted he was staggered: he had never heard a tale so bizarre. 'It's the very Devil, Andrew,' he remarked, and unknowingly coined the nick-name by which Crosse was later to become known among his friends: 'Devil' Crosse. The electrician, for his part, felt better that he had at last told someone else what had occurred. Although Southey could offer no solution, before he continued on his journey he encouraged Crosse to speak about it to other scientists. He was clearly convinced of his friend's sincerity and felt sure that other men of good purpose would give him a fair hearing.

On returning to Fyne Court, Crosse sat down in his laboratory and wrote a full report of the creation of the *Acari* which he despatched to the Electrical Society in London. There, his report was received with some scepticism, but it was decided to invite another electrician, a Mr W. H. Weeks of Sandwich in Kent, to repeat the experiments just as Crosse had described them. The matter was subsequently reported in the *Transactions of the London Electrical Society* (1838) and partially in *Annals of Electricity* (October 1836 – October 1837). Unfortunately Weeks did not publish a complete account of his experiments, only a summary of his results, but these notes do show he worked intelligently and thoroughly — and confirmed what Crosse had discovered.

Weeks took a number of precautions to ensure as far as humanly possible that no animal or insect life was present in the equipment. For instance, he baked his apparatus in an oven, used distilled water, filled his receivers (inverted over mercury troughs) with manufactured oxygen instead of air, and superheated his silicate solutions. Applying electrification, he said, he first saw the liquid in his vessel grow turbid; gelatinous matter collected around the negative wire of his battery which was immersed in the fluid, and finally one of the new insects emerged from the gelatine and ran off to a corner of the apparatus. The process took about a year and a half. When no electric current was used, however, none of the insects appeared. He also made quantitive experiments, and found that the number of *Acari* electrically produced varied, roughly, with the percentage of carbon in his solution.

While this unhurried and scientific study was going on, Crosse had inadvertently allowed news of his insects to leak out into the world at large. He instantly became famous.

As a result of the friendly appreciation he had received from Southey, Crosse had mentioned his discovery to several friends. He also discussed the matter with some acquaintances during one of his infrequent visits to Taunton. Among the group was the editor of *The Western Gazette* who listened in amazement to one of the most remarkable stories he had ever heard. Cornelia Crosse tells us the outcome of this encounter:

> Mr Crosse chanced ... to name the matter in the presence of the editor of a West of England paper, who immediately, *unauthorised*, but in a very friendly spirit, published an account of the experiment; which account quickly flew over England, and indeed Europe, satisfying at once the credulity of those who love the marvellous, and raising up a host of bitter and equally unreasoning assailants, whose personal attacks on Mr Crosse, and their misrepresentations of his views, were at once ridiculous and annoying.

The columns of the newspapers became full of voices raised in anger. One man described Crosse as 'a reviler of our holy religion', while another called him a 'disturber of the peace of families'. He was denounced as an atheist, a blasphemer, and a man who had presumptuously attempted to rival God in creating life. The lunatic fringe even began accusing him of being the cause of all manner of disturbances then current.

Poor Crosse, at heart still a man who wished to be left alone to his research, could only watch helplessly as his name became a by-word for eccentric science. In vain he protested that he had not set out to create life, nor had he

120

even claimed publicly to have done so — merely reported the strange thing which had occurred in the privacy of his laboratory. 'I have never ventured an opinion on the cause of their birth,' he replied to one correspondent, 'and for a very good reason — I was unable to form one.'

His mood of despair was to deepen further, as he noted in a letter to another friend (quoted by Cornelia Crosse) during the winter of 1836:

> I have met with so much virulence and abuse, so much calumny and misrepresentation, in consequence of these experiments that it seems, in this nineteenth century, as if it were a crime to have made them. For the sake of truth and the science which I follow, I must state that I am neither an atheist, nor a materialist, nor a self-imagined creator, but a humble and lowly reverencer of that Great Being of whose laws my accusers seem to have lost sight. It is my opinion that science is only valuable when employed as a means to a greater end. I attach no particular value to any experiments that I have made, and I care not if what I have done be entirely overthrown, if Truth is elicited. Though warmly attached to experimental philosophy, I have never for one moment imagined that it is possible to perform a single experiment which is absolutely perfect in itself, or indeed that we can carry out any train of such which are not more or less liable to objection.

Once such a controversy had been lit, however, the fire only increased. Even an impassioned lecture at the Royal Institute in 1837 by the renowned Michael Faraday, in which he condemned the harshness with which Crosse was being treated and urged a fair investigation into the appearances, did nothing to stop the furore. Faraday said that he himself had repeated the experiment and likewise produced the *Acari Crossii*, as he now proposed the new species should be named.

If Crosse was pleased at having achieved that summit of a scientist's life — having a discovery named after him — he revealed nothing except his continuing annoyance at being misrepresented in the press and his redoubled determination now to live an even more reclusive life beyond the stares of the curious. Speaking of those who maligned him, he said, 'By such I have been termed a self-imagined Creator. Man can neither create nor annihilate. To create is to form a something out of nothing; to annihilate is to reduce that something to nothing. The chemist plays with the substances brought under his notice; he decomposes; he recomposes; he is a humble imitator of Nature; to create or annihilate is not in his power.'

Crosse was clearly deeply hurt when it was suggested he was somehow responsible for having undermined religion with his work. 'I am sorry,' he wrote to another correspondent, 'that the faith of my neighbours can be overthrown by the claw of a mite. My poor little insects, the so-called *Acarus Galvanicus*, have had greatness thrust upon them: it was certainly not my intention that they should make themselves great.'

With the passing of the months it became increasingly clear to Crosse that no matter how much he protested, his notoriety was indestructible: perhaps with the passage of time the matter would be forgotten. He would withdraw from the controversy once and for all.

An exhaustive search through the newspapers, journals and scientific journals of the time shows that the electrician did indeed do just that. In fact, as far as I have been able to trace, he only made one further attempt to set the record straight — as late as August 1849 when he was approached by the leading historian, Harriett Martineau, who was busy assembling material for her *History of the Thirty Years' Peace*. She asked him quite simply for his version of the event which had become so widely discussed during the period she was treating.

Crosse, perhaps surprisingly because he wanted the matter forgotten, accepted the invitation, but clearly the events still rankled, for as he said in his opening remarks: 'You are welcome to publish it if you think proper, or thrust it into the fire, where many of those kind commentators on some of my experiments would gladly have thrust me.' As much of the letter is taken up with the details of the experiments I gave earlier, I should just like to quote one passage which summarises both Crosse's attitude and frame of mind at this time:

I can assure you most sacredly that I have never dreamed of any theory sufficient to account for their appearance. I confess that I was not a little surprised, and am so still, and quite as much as I was when the acari made their first appearance. Again, I have never claimed any merit as attached to these experiments. It was a matter of chance. I was looking for silicious formations, and animal matter appeared instead. The first publication of my original experiment took place entirely without my knowledge. Since that time, and surrounded by death and disease, I have fought my way in the different branches of the science which I so dearly love, and have endeavoured to be somewhat better acquainted with a few of its mysteries.

Harriet Martineau was clearly impressed by Crosse's sincerity of purpose and described in her book how his 'electric insects' were created. She commented, 'If allowed to remain in the enclosure, they perish. If let out as soon as they appear, they feed, reproduce their kind, and live till the first frost, which is always fatal to them'. She went on:

When the contempt and prejudice with which great discoveries are always received shall have subsided, it will be admitted that Mr Crosse has merely made known, in the simplest manner, appearances which presented themselves to him, propounding no theory, drawing no inferences, and attacking no established belief. While, for thirteen years, too many who might have tested his assertions have been merely expressing contempt of them, he and one or two more have been diversifying their experiments as much as they could, and found themselves occasionally rewarded by the appearance of acari.

These are results too serious and significant to be treated with either levity or anger; yet have they been received with too much of both. The objections made have been mostly of the *a priori* sort; and it is needless to say that they cannot withstand the evidence of experiment. Mr Crosse's invitation to the scientific part of society is to join him in ascertaining, by every possible variety and patience of experiment, what is the truth of the matter; and, till this is done, his information remains the best that can be had on a subject of unbounded philosophical significance. As such, its first proposal for attestation is an incident worthy of special notice in a history of the time.

Such a verdict, however, was not one that society in the

middle years of the nineteenth century — or history for that matter — was to accord to Andrew Crosse. In a few years his work was destined for oblivion, confined to a few footnotes and a collection of rapidly fading newspaper clippings. Nor were the last years of the electrician's life to offer much more to him personally: he was fated to become an almost total recluse in his Somerset home, often surrounded by unhappiness, and with only the comfort of a second marriage — following the death of his first wife after a lingering illness — to sustain him.

It is to these last years and a possible solution to the great mystery of Crosse's *Acari* that I shall devote my final chapter.

9

Requiem for a Mystery

According to *The Dictionary of National Biography*, 'After the notoriety gained by the publication of his accidental result, Crosse retired to Broomfield and led the life of a recluse, giving very desultory attention to his electrical experiments.' To be fair, the first half of this statement is certainly true — though Crosse's seclusion was interrupted from time to time, as we shall see — but it is also a fact that the electrician still had some quite remarkable contributions to make to science.

Life for him at Fyne Court was now far from easy. He was shunned by the local people, for the many things which had been alleged against him as a result of the *Acari* only seemed to confirm their opinion that he was a man to be avoided. On one occasion a group of men, suitably emboldened by drink, smashed his fences, fired some of his crops and killed a number of his livestock. There were others who hurled stones at him from behind his back whenever he tried to continue with his walks or rides across the Quantocks. Indeed, any journey beyond his estate became dangerous, and such was the atmosphere that only the most faithful of the servants stayed loyal to the master and his ailing wife.

At the height of the local fury against Crosse, a fanatical young clergyman from Bridgwater, the Reverend Philip Smith, even conducted a service of exorcism on the hills above Fyne Court in the hope that he would drive the wicked squire and his devils from the neighbourhood.

Whether Reverend Smith had come up to Broomfield of his own accord, or had been egged on by the group of country folk who gathered behind him as he stood looking down on the mansion, is unknown. However, there was no doubt that in the gloom of late afternoon the house looked sinister, as did the network of copper wires glinting in the last rays of the sunshine. Some of the group looked fearfully at them, expecting at any moment that the devils, Cob, Mob and Chittibob who were said to dance on them would appear.

Nothing stirred as the churchman opened his Bible and began to recite the service of Exorcism. Holding up a hand in the air, he indicated the darkened building beneath and shouted: 'Crosse is an atheist and a self-styled creator. He has sold his Divine Soul to Satan, and conjured up devils to dwell in the forests about our homes.'

The group of people behind Reverend Smith looked nervously at one another, and then back at Fyne Court. Still nothing moved.

Then, as the clergyman's voice began to recite the words of the exorcism, a man at the rear of the group heard something behind him. He turned and saw a rider coming towards him out of the gloom. He recognised the man at once: it was Squire Crosse. He turned to a companion and grunted fearfully 'It's 'im — "Devil" Crosse!' and took to his heels. As soon as the others had seen where the man had pointed, they, too, ran off.

Reverend Smith did not realise his congregation had fled until he heard the heavy breathing of Crosse's horse. The electrician looked at the young priest with a mixture of pity and resignation in his eyes.

'What are you doing here?' he asked, then turned to point behind him at the fleeing figures disappearing into the night. 'And why have they run away?'

The clergyman looked back at the rider defiantly, holding the Bible up before him. 'Criminal,' he spat. 'Reviler of our holy religion! Disturber of Christian peace. We came to ask Heaven's protection from you and your foulness!'

126

For a moment, Andrew Crosse stared at the wild-eyed young man in clerical black. He had seen the look before and heard the same words so many times. It would be pointless to argue. Instead, he simply wheeled away his horse and galloped off down the slope towards Fyne Court.

Crosse had, of course, been denounced from the pulpit in many churches both in Britain and Europe, but this was the first time a priest had actually come to his door. He had been accused of causing a potato blight which destroyed crops in both Somerset and Devon that year, but this was the first time he had heard anyone ask for God's protection *against* him. As he rode into his home that night, he must truly have felt that the whole world was against him.

Within the walls of his home, grief and anxiety were continually plaguing him, for as Kenyon wrote at this time, 'God Bless you, my dear Crosse — your life has been one of severe visitations, but God has given you the power of attaching your friends to you, and you cannot suffer without many a heart's feeling for you.' Sincerely as his old schoolfriend undoubtedly meant these words, it is sadly true that few of these 'friends', whoever they were, helped Crosse or visited him at Fyne Court, and those who gave him any support at this black period of his life were mostly scientists and other amateur electricians.

Cornelia Crosse tells us that the first Mrs Crosse was very ill at this period — her health no doubt affected by the problems besetting her husband — and Andrew's brother, Richard, who lived in an extraordinary house about three miles from Fyne Court, was also in failing health. By all accounts Richard Crosse was something of an eccentric: he was a passionate believer in the decimal system and had gone to the length of converting all his clocks so that they were divided into ten hours. His home was also built in the form of a double cube, each room being mathematically proportioned. None the less, the two brothers were close friends and would spend many hours in philosophic discussion, at which Andrew acknowledged Richard to be his peer.

Speaking of this time, the second Mrs Crosse prefers to draw a veil over it and writes, 'The truest and saddest part of a man's life is often that which it is not the business of a biographer to narrate.'

What we do know, however, is that Crosse became so unhappy about life in England, and the persecution he was suffering, not to mention financial problems, that he seriously considered leaving the country and living abroad. In a letter to W. H. Weeks, the man who had confirmed his findings about the *Acari*, he confided how low he felt:

It is very true that I have serious thoughts of going to the Continent for three years from the time of my starting, which cannot be before the spring of 1843. From the time of my birth to the present hour I have ever been far too careless in money transactions, and my love for science has not only led me to a considerable expense *directly*, but has, by calling nearly the whole of my attention elsewhere, prevented me from looking into my affairs with that scrutiny which is absolutely essential in a country establishment, and in the management of landed property. I have therefore, of course, been cheated tremendously, which I have to thank myself for.

Although I am MUCH ATTACHED to this place, yet in common prudence I must quit it for a time, and carry on my experiments on a more limited plan, and in a cheaper country than this. I am happy to say that my family will all be well provided for, and for myself it is of little consequence as to the increase or diminution of a few comforts, as I am very easily satisfied, and my life cannot extend to a much longer term. The income tax has put the finishing stroke to my determination.'

Crosse signed off, 'It is only in my power to wish, and I wish you all the happiness in this world, and humbly trust we may meet in a better.'

Determined though Crosse may have been, the poor health of both his wife and his brother entailed him constantly postponing these plans to emigrate. Then in January 1846, within four days of each other, both Mrs Crosse and Richard Crosse died.

With the deaths of the two people closest to him, Crosse no doubt felt he had suffered all he could. What more could life do to him? His own children had been sent away to school, and the remaining servants at Fyne Court saw less and less of him as he confined himself once more in his laboratory and carried on his experiments with electricity and electro-chemistry. He appreciated his own state of mind quite clearly, though, for he wrote:

> When misfortune oppresses, and the cares of life thicken around us, how delightful is it to retire into the recesses of one's own mind, and plan with a view to carrying out those scientific arrangements, with a humble hope of benefiting our country, improving our own understandings, and finding unspeakable consolation in the study of the boundless works of our Maker! Often have I, when in perfect solitude, sprung up in a burst of schoolboy delight at the instant of a successful termination of a tremblingly anticipated result. Not all the applause of the world could repay the real lover of science for the loss of such a moment as this.

In truth, however, the trauma of the death of his wife and brother seemed in a strange kind of way to stimulate him to a period of great activity and uncannily accurate prophecy of future scientific development.

In late 1846, for example, we find him writing that he hopes one day to be able to construct 'a battery at once cheap, powerful and durable, so I might say with Archimedes that I can move the world.' Here, it seems reasonable to conject, he forsaw the dry cell battery now so widely used in portable radios, cycle lamps, and so on.

He also turned his attention to using electricity for the purification of sea water and other fluids. To achieve this, he took two cylinders of dissimilar metals (zinc and iron) and placed them in two porous earthenware tubes, open at the top and closed at the bottom. The cylinders were connected by a copper ribbon, and the porous tubes, with the metals inverted in them, filled with water and then placed in the fluid to be purified. As Crosse explained: 'The application of this principle to wines and brandy has been attended with great success. It has the effect of softening the asperities of some wines by removing the predominance of bitartrate of potash; and in the case of the spirit distilled in imitation of French brandy, the improvement to be derived from using the process is remarkable.'

Having devised a way to improve liquids, he next

considered food stuffs. I quote from Mrs Crosse's *Memorials of Andrew Crosse*:

The antiseptic power of electrified water is very remarkable. Not only can it be preserved for years perfectly clear and fresh, but it has the power of restoring the most putrid substances to sweetness. Pieces of meat and the skins of animals in a state of putridity have been immersed in electrified water, and in a few hours rendered inodorous. Milk has also been kept sweet for three weeks in the middle of summer, by the application of electricity. On one occasion Mr. Crosse kept a pair of soles under the electric action for three months and at the end of that time they were sent to a friend, whose domestics knew nothing of the experiment. Before the cook dressed them her master asked her whether she thought they were fresh as he had some doubts. She replied that she was sure they were fresh; indeed she said she could swear that they were alive yesterday!! When served at table they appeared like ordinary fish; but when the family attempted to eat them they were found to be perfectly tasteless: the electric action had taken away all the essential oil, leaving the fish unfit for food. However, the process is exceedingly useful for keeping fish, meat, &c., fresh and *good* for ten days or a fortnight.

Mrs Crosse added that her husband also concluded at this time that 'electrified water might be drunk beneficially in cases of typhus and other fevers, and also could be used for baths.'

Still undisturbed in his remote laboratory, by the middle of 1847 Crosse had directed his attention to a theory concerning the growth of vegetation and the influence of electric action. He became convinced that such electric action was the cause of mineral substances being carried into, and forming component parts of, the vegetable kingdom. He conducted a remarkable experiment with two potatoes, one of which was planted in a pot of earth kept positively electrified, and the other maintained with negative electricity. The first flourished and grew; the second rapidly failed and became diseased.

Crosse deduced from this that negative electricity was injurious to all vegetables, and positive electricity most beneficial. When his theory was tried on a vine, one shoot being attached to the positive pole of a battery, and the other to the negative, the former shoot grew *over twice as long* as the latter, and produced grapes one third bigger. A similar experiment was tried with rose blooms, freshly cut, and the one connected to the negative pole drooped within a matter of hours, while that receiving positive electricity continued its freshness for nearly a fortnight.

Crosse also came to believe that the roots and leaves of plants were in opposite states of electricity and tried for some time to devise equipment to prove this theory. Writing in 1847 he said, 'I have no doubt in my own mind that electrical action is essential to vegetation; but little or nothing definite has been done in that department, in which men of science have taken very opposite views.'

Perhaps, though, the most remarkable of all his experiments were those in which he attempted to find a way of keeping blood pure for a lengthy period of time. In this, he was clearly pioneering the way for the modern blood bank and our use of blood transfusions. Crosse used pig's blood for his work, and in his most successful test — which was begun in February 1854 and not actually checked until February 1856, some months after his death — the blood remained perfectly fluid and its colour unaltered. The blood was kept constantly electrified by means of three pairs of plates connected to a sulphate of copper battery which was occasionally fed to maintain the action. If Crosse had lived to see the success of this test, it is interesting to conject where the results might have led him ...

The long years which Crosse spent in isolation left him as introspective and gloomy as ever, although with the passing of time he did seem to lose some of the bitterness which he felt over the affair of the *Acari Crossii*. After a long break, too, he began to travel again, and in 1848 returned to London for the first time in many years. The reason why is explained in a letter to a certain John Sealy of Bridgwater. It is addressed from Portman Square in London and dated July 1848:

I perfectly agree with you as to the glorious magnificence of the scenery of the Quantock Hills; but where are those that

131

rendered it dear to me gone? I feel that I have no home, that I am cast as a weak vessel on the billows of the ocean, and all spots of land are now much the same to me. When I am at Broomfield I have not a soul to speak to, servants excepted. In fact I am quite desolate, and am now thrown on the aids of science ... with the exception of your family, and one or two others, I have no intimacies in the country. In this huge metropolis there is a power of selecting one's acquaintances beyond that in any other situation.

Crosse's words were to prove prophetic once more, for early in 1849, while dining with a small group of people associated with scientific research, he was introduced to a beautiful dark-haired young woman named Cornelia Burns. Chance placed the ageing electrician and the intelligent Cornelia, who was still in her twenties, opposite each other at the table, and they were soon wrapt in conversation. Cornelia was unashamed in her admiration for Crosse, saying that she had been interested in science since her youth and had actually cut out scraps from the newspapers describing his work. The man from Somerset was clearly taken by this young woman with her enthusiasm for his special subject, and she, for her part, admitted that 'it was with no common feelings that I looked upon the man whose power in wielding that mysterious agent, electricity, had so excited my imagination.' During the evening Crosse also recited some of his poetry, and before they parted, Cornelia knew they were destined for each other. She later confided in her *Memorials*, 'I had expected to find what I reverenced — a follower of science: I found what I worshipped — a poet.'

After several more meetings in London, Crosse invited Cornelia to come and visit his home. The experiences of a young town girl confronted for the first time with the home of a reclusive country scientist were unforgettable, as she tells us:

At Fyne Court Mr Crosse was surrounded by a perfect chaos of apparatus. Certainly the old house had more a philosophic than a domestic air about it. The family plate was occasionally called on to make contributions to the crucible, which, with the aid of the laboratory furnace, converted tea-pots, tankards, and old-fashioned spoons into *chemically pure* silver in a very short space of time! A great deal of the glass and china of the house was not suffered to remain in vulgar use, but was dedicated to nobler purposes, and was formed into batteries or other electrical arrangements. The rooms generally seemed in a process of resolving themselves into laboratories or other kinds of scientific dens. You were perfectly comfortable, perfectly at home, under the hospitable roof; but, to speak in geological language, the house appeared to be rather in a *transition* state.

There is a story that after Mr Crosse had finished the sixth or seventh furnace in his laboratory, he said, with an air of great satisfaction, 'I consider *now* that my house is thoroughly furnished'. The old place had got into a terrible habit of wanting repair. In a storm, the slates of the roof seemed as if positively electrified, and flew right and left in mutual repulsion. Mr Crosse's large philosophical room had fallen down. Dr Buckland, at the inauguration meeting of the Archaeological Society at Taunton, gave a humorous description of this accident, attributing the circumstance to the effects of misguided lightning, which the electrician was supposed to have trifled with. The facts of the case, however, were more prosaic. A bad architect and a dishonest builder were the real foundation of the mischief!

Crosse took great pains to show Cornelia all his apparatus, conducting her from underground cellars where agates were being formed in electrified solutions, through the mass of wires and batteries in his 'electrical room' and even into 'a mysterious chamber dimly lit by a magician-looking lamp in which there was no sound save the ceaseless and regular dropping of water helping the growth of crystals'. It must have seemed eerie and even a little frightening, but Cornelia was evidently delighted and already knew she was going to be making her home here.

When Cornelia returned to London, she determined that the next time Crosse came to the capital she would do her best to get him circulating in society, and thereby perhaps draw him out of his introspection a little. She succeeded, despite the electrician's initial reluctance, and during the winter of 1850 he records in a letter that he attended several balls, a number of gatherings and dinners and one party 'filled with wild and talented people'. Cornelia even got him to the theatre on several occasions. However, the encounters he evidently enjoyed the most were with other scientists and in their company, and with their encouragement, he felt that not all his lonely experimenting had been in vain.

On July 22, 1850, Crosse and Cornelia were married in London at the Church of St Marylebone. After a honeymoon spent in the Lake District, they returned to Broomfield where the young wife was determined to see Fyne Court restored to something like its former glory. By her own account, she quickly settled into a domestic life and was not unduly perturbed by the isolation of the place. Crosse busied himself again in his laboratory.

'There was plenty of work for everyone,' the new Mrs Crosse wrote. 'Batteries had to be taken to pieces or renewed; zinc rods to be cast, copper cylinders fitted for perhaps 150 bottles, which, with broken necks, stood up as battery jars. He was kind enough to make me his pupil, so that we had plenty of employment; indeed the days were never long enough.'

The following year, 1851, the couple went back up to London to attend the Great Exhibition at Crystal Palace, and Crosse was an interested member of the audiences at numerous scientific meetings and lectures. He would not, though, allow himself to be talked into addressing any of the gatherings.

Crosse's health, which had never been good, was now beginning to fail, and although he enjoyed country walks whenever he felt strong enough, he was happiest working quietly or supervising the management of Fyne Court. Occasional visitors came to see the couple,* and Crosse widened his list of correspondents to include some of the new friends he had made in London through Cornelia. In 1852 we find him perceptively writing to one of these people, 'The Maker of the Universe seems to have

* One of these visitors was the Reverend John Eagles, another of Crosse's former schoolfriends who stayed at Fyne Court in 1852, and the following year, in January 1853, published an account of his visit in *Blackwood's Magazine* entitled 'Letter to Eusebius about Many Things'. A number of important facts for this biography have been drawn from Eagle's essay.

established *change* as one of the first laws of Nature. Nothing sleeps; and the gold of California and Australia will establish two new and mighty empires to last, each for a time, and then to fall into the ruins of their predecessors. My experiments are still progressing, and produce their *little* changes ...'

The following winter proved a long and cold one, and Crosse and his young wife were cooped up in Fyne Court for months on end. The electrician seemed to fall back into his former melancholy and Cornelia tells us of a strange incident which occurred one night.

Crosse had been sitting before the fire, deep in thought, when he suddenly announced: 'I have often thought that this world is a place of punishment, where we are called upon to suffer for sins committed in some former state. But we know nothing of the past — of the present — of the future — except relatively; we can only pray.'

As he finished speaking, the room was suddenly illuminated by a great flash of light and followed by a sharp, crackling explosion. 'What was that?' Cornelia gasped out, as another blinding flash and crackling sound followed. For several minutes both she and Crosse sat dumbfounded in their chairs as the illuminations and sounds continued. Then, gradually, they abated and all was still again. Crosse sprang up and flung open a window: he saw snow was falling outside. But what had this to do with the mystery?

It was not until Crosse went to examine his equipment that he found the answer. Inadvertently, he had left the brass receiving balls which were attached to the wire network close together. So when the snow had begun to fall the wires had been charged with electricity and all the appearances of a thunderstorm had been mimicked by the equipment, although nothing of the sort had taken place. The strange juxtaposition of what he had been saying and the electrical display was not lost on Crosse.

In the spring of 1853, the Crosses made another journey up to London, the electrician having been coaxed from his retreat by Michael Faraday who was anxious to discuss electricity with him. In a book which Mrs Crosse published some years after the death of her husband, *Red-Letter Days of*

My Life (1892) in which she collected articles she had written for the *Temple Bar* magazine about distinguished men and women of her times she knew, she mentions this meeting of the two scientists.

Faraday gave Crosse a conducted tour through his 'workshops' as he called his laboratories at the Royal Institution. 'Faraday let us have a peep into the 'froggery', wrote Mrs Crosse, 'a dismal sort of oubliette in this castle of science. Here, tradition says, those hapless creatures were kept for repeating Galvani's experiments on animal electricity.'

The electrician from Broomfield was fascinated by this place, and probed Faraday with questions. He had heard of Galvani's experiments, he said, and in particular the theory that inanimate bodies — including human corpses — could be reanimated with electrical currents fed into the muscles. Faraday, too, had been fascinated by such ideas and had taken part in experiments utilising dead frogs as the subjects to be animated. He said it was a matter much in the public mind at the moment, and had even inspired a book he had perused recently from one of the circulating libraries to which he subscribed. It was called *Frankenstein*, and was by

Michael Faraday's laboratory at the Royal Institution around which Andrew Crosse was conducted. The two men became firm friends.

the wife of the late poet Percy Shelley. He was much taken with such novels, he said, as they diverted his mind from the pressures of his work. Crosse replied that he rarely had time for reading, and had no particular taste for novels. The men passed on in silence.

Neither could have had the slightest intimation that the man from Somerset had also played a part in the creation of the book Faraday had so casually mentioned.

The tour continued with an inspection of Faraday's new laboratory and then on into the Institution's theatre, where later the couple from Somerset were to hear Faraday speak. The two scientists continued deep in conversation until finally and reluctantly they had to part.

Cornelia Crosse tells us that her husband and Faraday met again several times during their stay in London, and another topic which engaged their interest was spiritualism, then much in the news. Crosse thought very little of 'spirit-rapping, mesmerisms, table-turnings, &c.', she said, but Faraday found himself inexorably dragged into the controversy:

Faraday was pestered with applications and letters from people who believed that 'a new force' had been discovered, and expected him to explain it scientifically. 'Poor electricity is made accountable for half the follies of the age,' said Faraday one day when we were talking over the new craze. He invited my husband to accompany him to a *seance*, where the following incident occurred. A girl present, who was said to be in a state of clairvoyance, was supposed to manifest extraordinary emotion when, as directed, Dr Faraday turned the apex of a rock crystal towards her. But the girl could see the crystal, and the obvious conclusion was — that she was in collusion with the giver of the *seance* and was acting a part. It was pretended that the action of her ordinary senses was in abeyance, and that in fact her eyes saw nothing outwardly. Mr Crosse handed his hat to Dr Faraday to use as a screen before the object; this was no sooner done than the clairvoyante failed utterly to respond to the movements of the crystal. There were other exhibitions, which under the test of common sense, failed equally; the whole thing was a perfect fiasco, quite unworthy of the serious consideration of scientific men. Faraday often took occasion to remark 'on the tendency there is in the human mind to deceive

137

ourselves in regard to all we wish, and the lack of all real educational training of the judgment.'

Much though Andrew Crosse had enjoyed his sojourn in London, he was a very tired man when he returned to Fyne Court. He was, after all, nearly seventy years old. For the following year he lived in almost total seclusion at Broomfield, Cornelia Crosse taking over the role of running the household with quiet efficiency.

Some of his former strength seems to have returned by the spring of 1855, and again he and Cornelia paid a brief visit to London. This time they spent their days quietly, entertaining their trusted old friends, Kenyon and Eagles. Mrs Crosse notes in her memoirs that though none of the three men could know it, this was to be the last occasion they ever spent together.

Back at Fyne Court in May, Crosse began an experiment designed to shave grains off a solid piece of chemically pure gold by electric action. For this he employed a galvanic battery which electrified a vessel containing a solution of sulphuric acid and distilled water in which the gold piece stood on a square of white marble. According to Cornelia Crosse:

The result was most conclusive. In former experiments, with a less powerful battery, he had succeeded in breaking off six grains, this time he knocked off no less than twenty-three grains. He was greatly pleased at the success of the experiment, which was certain before the lapse of twenty-four hours; but he did not take it apart, for he resolved to leave it at work as long as the battery continued strong enough to cause a powerful evolution of gas. This was the last scientific act of his life.

On the morning of May 26, Crosse suddenly felt giddy as he was dressing. He threw himself down on the bed and felt a great stabbing pain on his left hand side. 'Cornelia,' he cried out, 'I have a paralytic seizure; send for Mr King.' As his wife stood horrified, trying to convince herself he was mistaken, Crosse went on even more emphatically, 'My dear wife, bear it, as I must bear it. Do not deceive yourself, this is my death-stroke.'

Because of its isolation, it was almost three hours before the doctor reached Fyne Court, and in the intervening time the stricken electrician had uttered words which Cornelia found unforgettable. 'If by moving my finger I could restore myself to perfect health,' he said, 'and to the certainty of several years of life, I would not do it if I knew it to be contrary to the will of God.'

For several days and nights, Cornelia Crosse sat by her husband's bedside as he slowly sank towards death. 'He rarely slept,' she noted, 'and through the dark hours of night, or during the early dawn of those bright summer mornings, he would talk to me on subjects of the highest and holiest interest. At times his mind seemed intensified by his illness, his conversation was such that it was a strain upon my own mental powers to follow him. I could almost say that he anticipated and realised the greatness of immortality.'

As Crosse lay dying, a few of the country people came nervously to the doors of Fyne Court to enquire how he was. Some were obviously still fearful of his reputation, and hurried quickly away once they had been told. Others felt they had perhaps been hasty in their judgment, but still could not look at the wires which led into his silent laboratory without a shudder at what they believed had once gone on here. It was clear even then that the electrician's notoriety would now go with him to the grave.

On the morning of July 6, Crosse awoke in terrible pain and took Cornelia's hand for one last time. He seemed far off, possessed by some terrible knowledge he could not possibly explain. Drawing a deep breath he spoke a final lingering sentence. 'My dear, the utmost extent of human knowledge is but comparative ignorance.'

Then the white-haired old man sank back on his pillow and died in the very room in which he had been born 71 years before. Three days later, at a simple ceremony, attended by just his family and a few friends, Andrew Crosse was buried in Broomfield Church.

One man, in the group of local people who stood watching beyond the churchyard wall, crossed himself and muttered a quiet prayer.

'God, let him rest in peace, and never more trouble us with the devils or the lightning.'

The Amen spoken by those around him echoed quietly across the sun-dappled Quantock Hills.

*   *   *

Although there were no more experiments carried out at Fyne Court after Crosse's death, his reputation continued to be a subject of speculation and rumour for many years. Stories, some wild exaggerations and others plainly untrue, circulated about what he had done in the secrecy of his laboratory, and helped keep his memory alive, at least in local history if not in that of the nation. Because, as I have intimated, he left so few reports of his work and conclusions, his place in the annals of science has mainly been confined to footnotes where the early years of electricity are concerned. It is a situation that has not changed to this day.

There are stories still told in Somerset that not long after Crosse's death, a group of local people broke into his laboratory one night and smashed all his equipment so that no one else should ever continue his devilish experiments. It is said, too, that the copper wires strung across his estate were vandalised by unknown hands, and there was a more mysterious story still that Crosse had managed to create a kind of rudimentary wireless set powered by electricity which enabled him to send messages over long distances: this, too, was destroyed by the pillagers. We know he had predicted the wireless telegraph: if he had actually *created* one, he would have been many years ahead of Marconi — but such an idea is only speculation and unsubstantiated by any facts.*

* A modern writer, Colin Cooper, has used the legend of Crosse as the basis of his novel, *The Thunder and Lightning Man* (1968), in which the central figure, Daniel Eldervale, uses his electrical knowledge to create a radio transmitter years ahead of its time. This amateur scientist also inadvertently gives life to a breed of insects known as *Acarus Galvanicus*, and finds himself as hounded and persecuted as Andrew Crosse. It is an interesting and thought-provoking novel. To my knowledge, only one other piece of fiction has been written based on 'The Wizard of the Quantocks' and this is the short story, 'The Electric Vampire' by F. H. Power which appeared in *The London Magazine* of October 1910 and is reproduced in the Appendix.

What we do know beyond doubt is that in 1898 a sudden and unexpected fire broke out at Fyne Court which completely gutted the splendid mansion — destroying everything except, perversely, Crosse's 'electrical room' — and left it uninhabitable for the remaining members of the family. Perhaps because of the continuing notoriety attached to the property and its former owner, they were quietly happy to move away from Broomfield. Only now, three-quarters of a century later, have permanent residents returned to the estate since it was taken over by the National Trust.

As this book has set out to show, Crosse has never received any credit for his scientific achievements or the influence he had on Mary Shelley's creation of *Frankenstein*. Moreover, it has been no surprise to me that for years that fine actor, Peter Cushing, has been considered by cinema experts to most nearly resemble the authoress's idea of her scientist who created life. The physical similarity between Andrew Crosse and Peter Cushing is, I believe, immediately obvious from comparing their portraits.

Nevertheless, the most puzzling aspect of all in this story is

The amazing likeness between Andrew Crosse and Peter Cushing, who has become widely recognised as the actor to most accurately portray Frankenstein as Mary Shelley envisaged him, is immediately evident in these pictures.

how did this obscure amateur scientist seemingly create life? *Where* did the *Acari* come from and were they a known species? And, perhaps most important of all, were they born naturally or by scientific process?

The simple answer which has most often been advanced is that the ova from the insects hatched were, despite all Crosse's precautions, introduced into his equipment at an early stage of the experiment and there activated into life by the process taking place.

In 1934, for instance, an authority on *Acari*, Dr A. C. Oudemans of Arnhem, made a study of the mystery and plumped for this explanation. He said that in his opinion the insects were the commonplace *Glyophagus domesticus*, which is very tenacious of life and capable of getting into tins which appear to be hermetically sealed. Plausible though this theory is, I do not think it satisfies all the details which I have included here of the experiments.

Rupert T. Gould in his book *Oddities* (1928), also examined the mystery and believed it was possible Crosse might have just been misled by appearances:

> It is quite possible to 'grow' artificial forms, from dead matter, which simulate living bodies in a positively uncanny way. Artificial 'plants', for example, can be grown (in certain solutions) which, although formed by a purely mechanical process — osmosis — have every appearance of life, and can even imitate the properties and movements of organic cells. The 'osmotic growths' produced by Dr Stephane Leduc of Nantes not only present the cellular structure of living matter, but reproduce such functions as the absorption of food, metabolism and the excretion of waste products.

> In spite of the precautions taken by Crosse and Weeks, it is, of course, impossible to disprove the assertion that their acari were hatched in the course of their experiments, having found their way into the apparatus as ova — the same cry of 'faulty technique' that has been raised (in my submission with more force) against such experimenters as Bastian.

Even so, Mr Gould concluded that, like Andrew Crosse, he could offer no positive opinion or explanation.

Perhaps, though, the most intriguing of all theories is that advanced in Valentine Dyall's *Unsolved Mysteries* (1954), in which it is suggested the insects might have been creatures from another world!

Dyall bases this idea on the works of Dr Immanuel Velikovsky, who suggested in his controversial book *Worlds in Collision* (1900) that conditions which are poisonous to all life on earth might be perfectly normal on other worlds and there generate life forms of their own. Could Crosse's *Acari* be such a life form transported to earth, Dyall asks?

According to Velikovsky, the planet Venus was formed by a comet which erupted out of another planet many thousands of years ago. The tail of this comet, he said, contained a mass of poisonous gases in which there were living creatures collected from the face of the 'mother' planet during the eruption.

Later, at about 1,500 B.C., the comet arrived near Earth and made several passes, which violently disrupted the world's rotation and at the same time its immense electrical power became alive and caused part of the gaseous tail to become detached and fall to earth, there depositing its cargo of creatures. Velikovsky believes this shower caused the plague which struck Egypt according to the Book of Exodus in the Bible.

In Dyall's opinion:

On the basis of Mr Velikovsky's theory, it might be reasonably suggested that ova transported to the Earth by a meteor are able to attach themselves to certain materials here and continue to exist — perhaps in a state of suspended animation — and that under the right conditions — perhaps including the discharge of electricity — living cells could develop from such an ova.

The piece of oxide or iron from Mount Vesuvius which Crosse used in his experiments may have contained ova from a long-forgotten meteor: by coincidence the 'poisonous' solution he used could be approximated to the atmosphere of the planet of origin and the gases in the comet's tail. When immersed in their natural 'atmosphere' the ova 'breathed again' — and produced the unknown insects.'

Exciting as this theory is, it does not take account of the fact that Crosse generated his insects with materials other

143

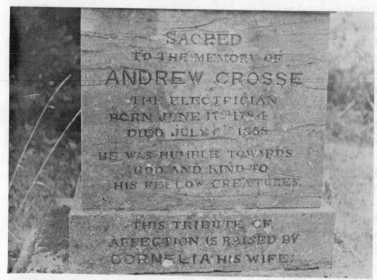

The inscription on Andrew Crosse's tomb — the only memorial to his life and work.

Fyne Court today — now renovated as the headquarters of a conservation and wild life centre.

than the samples from Mount Vesuvius. So we are left once more with the mystery as impenetrable as when we began.

Personally, I doubt we shall solve this strange enigma of science — perhaps one of the strangest of all on our records — until we know much more about what generates life and maybe even the secret of existence itself. Perhaps, as Crosse himself once noted, some future disciple of science will stumble on the answer just as he stumbled on the *Acari Crossii?*

As we have seen, Andrew Crosse was a strange, complex, yet bold and dedicated man who wanted no memorial and was happy in his adversity because of his devotion to science. He foresaw some of the possibilities of electricity long before his contemporaries, and in his own particular way contributed towards this advance, though little credit has ever been given to him.

My search for him in the hills of Somerset, in the archives of history, and in the tales of local folklore, has been a fascinating and rewarding one. All the time, I have been reminded of a quote that he made towards the end of his life, 'I think there is more romance in real life than was ever imagined by the most extravagant writer of fiction.'

Can there now be any doubt that this extraordinary man proved his own words? For me, 'The Man Who Was Frankenstein' not only inspired Mary Shelley's literary masterpiece — but in his life outdid even that great work of fiction.

Bridgwater, Somerset —
Boxford, Suffolk, 1974–9.

Appendix

I

The Island of Ellattosis

By Andrew Crosse

(This strange but incomplete short story with its elements of Science Fiction and fantasy was written by Crosse about 1818. It was discovered in manuscript form among his papers by his second wife, Cornelia.)

As I was reclining comfortably in an easy elbow-chair in my study, in the remote part of a lone country house, a cheerful wood fire blazing brightly before me, and the candles standing unlighted on a small reading table, though the increasing intensity of the evening shadows had long reminded me of my neglect, I could not be but struck at the contrast of the comforts which surrounded me, with the rude howling of the blast, as it swelled or died away amongst the shapeless masses of wood which environed the mansion, and which were scarcely discernible through the window, not merely on account of the approach of night, but from the hasty pattering of large drops of rain against the casement, which the violence of the gale alone prevented from descending in a settled shower. How many poor wretches thought I, are at this instant exposed to the fury of the tempest; houseless, penniless, without food, or sufficient to cover them, sinking under every sort of distress and disease. Perhaps a ship just returning from a long voyage laden with the wealth of the Indies, and filled with

146

passengers ardently desirous to welcome their native land, now strikes upon a hidden rock, and, in lieu of an endearing and hospitable reception, is ushered into horrors, whirlpools, and destruction, — whilst I, quietly seated in my chair, stretch my legs at my ease, and — stop, cries Recollection. Death will soon stretch your legs, and whether one is suffocated in a muddy ditch, drowned in the ocean, or pines away from a feather bed, with half a score of sage-looking doctors, mumbling politics in a corner, still Death is Death, and bow to it we must. Dreadful and tremendous decree, thought I, could not some other less agonising method of causing the disappearance of the human race have been determined? Scarce had the impious thought suggested itself, when a thick mist instantly filled the room; the howling of the wind subsided, the rain ceased to patter, the fire in the grate no longer crackled, nor did the flame move. All was breathlessly still, and a horrible expectation came over me of something unutterable.

On casting my eyes towards the lower part of the room, I clearly discovered the head of a venerable old man, whose white beard seemed to unite with the thick mist which pervaded the apartment, but which had not the power of concealing from my view his majestic though stern countenance. 'Worm,' cried he, 'canst thou pretend to know the events which take place in other regions? In the remote Isle of Elattosis, death is unheard of, and yet terror and anxiety are not more strangers to its inhabitants than they are to those of your regions.'

'How can this be?' I ventured humbly to breathe.

'See,' cried he; 'know by what no one can bequeath — experience.'

Immediately my sight failed me, and methought I sank into an ocean of waters, which seemed to bubble round my ears. In a few seconds, as I imagined, I found myself standing alone on the sandy shore of an apparently fertile country, whose swelling hills, variegated with wood, meadow, and corn land, rose one behind the other, till the whole was blended in a dark blue horizon. I had but little time for reflection, when a man dressed somewhat like an English mariner came up to me, seeing I was a stranger, and saluted me in courteous terms, to my utter amazement, in the ancient Greek tongue. As I had had some knowledge of the language flogged into me when a boy, although I had not much idea of chattering it, I was enabled, after a little consideration, to enter into some sort of conversation with him.

'Pray,' said I, rather abruptly, for I had not learned to be very civil during my sojourn in England, 'what the devil is the name of this queer-looking country?'

'Friend,' replied he, calmly, 'it is the Island of Elattosis, and you are the only individual whom I ever met with who was ignorant of it. I suppose you have sailed from some of the distant isles which lie at the north-west of this land?'

To this I assented with a nod, as I thought it the wisest course to pursue, and I was used to humbug in my own country, and made it a rule, as seldom as possible, to appear ignorant of anything.

'Sir,' said he, 'I am a captain of a small merchantman, and am well acquainted with these north-west islands, the Eikosi, the dress of whose inhabitants, I must confess, does not much resemble yours; and yet I know not from what other country you can have arrived.'

'Captain', returned I with a bold face, 'I allow I am clothed in a strange dress, but it is the consequence of a wager, which I shall lose if I adopt any other during the next three days, at the end of which period I intend to resume the dress of my own country.' I could not avoid reflecting on the inconvenience of one falsehood, which becomes necessarily the parent of a host of others.

The Captain, observing me look serious, said with much kindness, 'Come, sir, as you are at all events a stranger in this land, and if you can put up with a sailor's fare, you had better accompany me home'. To this I gladly assented, with thanks for his hospitality; and we set off on our walk. As we proceeded, after crossing a few fields, we came to an open road, bounded on one side by a down or common, entirely covered by what I imagined to be a species of moss. On stooping down to examine it, I was surprised to find it consisted of a kind of moss, each stem of which exactly resembled an oak-tree in miniature, with its leaves and

branches complete. Accordingly, I knelt down, and applied
a pair of pocket scissors to half-a-dozen stems, intending to
cut them off.

'Stop,' cries the Captain, 'what are you about to do? It is
not the custom here, for strangers to destroy the timber on
a gentleman's estate.'

'Timber!' cried I; 'surely, you don't call this brushy moss,
timber?'

The Captain shook his head, and made no answer, but
looked as though he suspected I was not in my right senses.
Finding that something was wrong, I pocketed my scissors,
and we continued our walk, till he came to a dwelling-house
of moderate size; this, my companion informed me, was his
home. 'My family,' said he, 'is but small. It consists of an old
father, a sick wife, and two children. My wife is so
exceedingly ill, that I am obliged to make use of a
magnifying power of 17 to discover her; but the doctor
gives me great hopes that she will be restored to her original
size. As for my poor old father, he is so reduced by age and
ill health, that he does not exceed 15 inches in height at
present.'

Here my astonishment was extreme, and I began to fear
that I had gotten into the company of a maniac. On our
arrival at the Captain's house, we were met by two chubby-
faced children, who stared at me with great surprise.

'How is your mother, my dears?' said the captain, to the
eldest.

'Oh, father, she is much better. I have looked in the glass
in which she is kept, and she is grown to the size of a broad
bean.'

'Heaven be praised!' said the worthy Captain, 'bring her
to me, John, carefully.' John was in an instant out of sight,
and soon returned with a half-pint tumbler in his hand, in
which the Captain desired me to look. No language can
describe the surprise I felt on discovering a minute female
figure dressed in a loose robe, and not exceeding an inch in
height. This little fairy form was walking rapidly round the
bottom of the glass.

'Ah, poor thing!' said the Captain, 'she is not yet large
enough to make her wants known by her voice. Put her

safely on the mantelpiece, my boy, and tell the nurse to drop into the glass some grains of boiled rice. But I beg pardon, sir,' said my host, 'for my apparent neglect. Our dinner must by this time be ready; pray walk this way;' and I followed him into a plain but neatly furnished apartment, where we partook of a boiled leg of mutton, and some mashed turnips and potatoes.

At this point, Andrew Crosse left off his fascinating story. It seems possible that Cornelia Crosse could have read it during her husband's life-time for she records his intentions for the rest of the tale in her *Memorials of Andrew Crosse*: 'I had proceeded so far in my story,' said Mr Crosse, 'when I dashed down my pen, conscious of the absurdity of attempting to describe any state of things so unnatural, that death and destruction should not be known; in truth, I could not, for I had myself violated the plan, and allowed the existence of death, in the fact of the food they eat; for, even if I had made them out to be vegetarians, still there would have been destruction going on; and so indeed would it be, should I but suffer them to breathe the very air, filled as it is with invisible life. This rude attempt of mine taught me one lesson — that is to say, how impossible it is for us to realise anything out of our limited experience of conditional truth.'

Appendix

II

The Electric Vampire

By F. H. Power

(This short story appeared in The London Magazine *of October 1910 with the accompanying Editor's note: 'The following short story, though of course but a figment of the imagination, is yet founded on fact. Over seventy years ago (in 1836, to be precise), a Mr Crosse astonished the British Association by reading a paper on electro-crystallisation, in which he described how he obtained living electrical insects, called acari, by artificial means — namely, by a voltaic battery, certain acids, and red oxide of iron. His experiments were closely watched by the leading scientists of the day, but Crosse himself gave them up, owing to the excited attitude of a section of the public, who assailed him with much bitterness for carrying out experiments which they considered it a "crime" to make.')*

I was at breakfast when the note reached me. 'My dear Charles,' it ran — 'I shall be glad if you can come round to my place tonight, as I have something to show you, which I think will interest you. I have also asked Vane.'

It did not take a moment for me to make up my mind to go. Dr Vane and I often spent an evening at George Vickers's house. We were bachelors, and as we were all fond of things scientific, the time passed very pleasantly — so pleasantly that very often it was two or three o'clock in the morning before he saw us off his premises.

During the day I found myself speculating as to what our

friend intended to show us. I recalled some of the weird and fascinating electrical experiments he had performed in his laboratory. 'I bet it's another experiment with electricity,' I said to myself, but I was only partly correct.

I arrived at the house about six o'clock, and found Vane had already arrived, and, as usual, had taken the easiest armchair in which to rest his lean body. Our host, with his ruddy, smiling face, stood with his back to the fireplace.

'I'm glad you have come, Charlie,' he said. 'You will be able to relieve me from that living mark of interrogation.' And he nodded towards the doctor, who sat twirling an imaginary moustache.

'Well, why can't he indicate what he has dragged us round here for?' the doctor asked plaintively. 'And fancy having as an excuse that he doesn't want to spoil my appetite for dinner!'

'Eh, what?' I ejaculated.

'Oh, now you are going to start. For goodness' sake find something else to talk about until we have had something to eat,' said Vickers, and he suggested aeroplanes.

We let him have his own way, and very soon after sat down to dinner. Our conversation during the meal would have been dry to many, but it was after our own hearts, and never flagged for a moment. The doctor's speciality was biology. My hobby is chemistry, and it was through an explosion which nearly blinded me that I first made his acquaintance, and subsequently introduced him to George Vickers.

At last George leaned back in his chair, and, lighting a cigar, said:

'You fellows, of course, want to know what on earth I am keeping up my sleeve. Before I show you, I want you to listen to this short extract from a series of lectures given by a man named Noad, and published in 1844.'

He fetched the book, and read:

' "It was in the course of his experiments in electro-crystallisation that that extraordinary insect about which so much public curiosity has been expended, was first noticed by Mr Crosse." '

Here Vickers looked up from the volume, and remarked:

'Mr Crosse I might say, was a gentleman who stood foremost as one of the individuals in this country who have distinguished themselves by their researches in atmospheric electricity.'

He turned to the book again:

' "In justice to this talented individual, who was most shamefully and absurdly assailed by some ignorant people on account of this insect, and who underwent much calumny and misrepresentation in consequence of experiments 'which in this nineteenth century it seems a crime to have made,' I shall give a detailed account of that experiment in which the Acarus first made its appearance." '

'Here follows,' said George, 'a minute description of the apparatus Crosse used. Briefly a basin containing practically a saturated solution of soluble silica is placed in a funnel, and a piece of flannel hangs over the side of the basin and acts as a syphon. The liquid falls in drops on a piece of porous red oxide of iron from Vesuvius, kept constantly electrified by a voltaic battery.'

Again he turned to the book and read:

' "On the fourteenth day from the commencement of the experiment, Mr Crosse observed through a lens a few small whitish excrescences or nipples projecting from about the middle of the electrified iron, and nearly under the dropping of the fluid above. On the eighteenth day these projections enlarged, and seven or eight filaments, each of them longer than the excrescence from which it grew, made their appearance on each of the nipples. On the twenty-second day, these appearances were more elevated and distinct; and on the twenty-sixth day each figure assumed the form of a *perfect insect* standing erect on a few bristles which formed its tail. Till this period Mr Crosse had no notion that these appearances were any other than an incipient mineral formation, but it was not until the twenty-eighth day, when he plainly perceived these little creatures move their legs, that he felt any surprise. In a few days they separated themselves from the stone, and moved about at pleasure. They appeared to feed by suction." ... Mr Crosse adds: "*I have never ventured an opinion as to the cause of their birth;* and for a very good reason — I was unable to form one." '

Vickers shut the book up.

'There's a lot more about it, but I think I have read all that is necessary. If either of you would like some more information on those early experiments, you will find it in the "Transactions of the Electrical Society".'

There was silence whilst we puffed at our cigars. At length, Dr Vane said:

'I was under the impression that subsequent experimentalists were not so successful as Mr Crosse?'

Vickers smiled enigmatically.

'If you will just come this way, I fancy I shall be able to prove to you that at least one other experimentalist has been fairly successful.' And beckoned us to follow him.

I had often been in his laboratory, but to my surprise he led us to a room at the top of the house, and, as he inserted the key, drew our attention to the Yale lock.

'I rely on you chaps to keep to yourselves what I am going to show you, because I am preparing a paper on this experiment, and I want to surprise 'em,' he said, and pushed the door open.

Dr Vane, with an eager look on his face, entered boldly. I followed close behind, and I remembered wondering why George, usually so unemotional, appeared to be in a state of suppressed excitement.

And then I saw what it was. May I, a man, be forgiven if I trembled from head to foot!

On a low plain wood table was a sheet of some metal about four feet square. From a cistern fixed above, and pierced by many minute holes, some liquid dropped on the slab incessantly. But these things I barely noticed, for my attention was riveted to the centre of that slab, on which sprawled a creature which I can only liken to an immense spider, its length being about two feet.

Two legs appeared from behind each side of the head, and four longer ones — they must have been nearly as long as the body — at the back. Projecting from its head, where you would expect to find the mouth, was a trunk-like object which went in and out like the trunk of a fly. All over the

'I saw what it was. May I, a man, be forgiven if I trembled from head to foot!' An illustration by Philip Baynes for 'The Electric Vampire' from The London Magazine.

body about an inch apart long filaments stood out. Its colour was drab, and it was apparently covered with slime. Its eyes were like the eyes of an owl, and never blinked.

We stared at the fearsome object in dead silence.

Vickers was the first to speak.

'Pretty, isn't it?' he said, with a laugh, but the laugh seemed strangely out of place.

I glanced at the doctor. His hands were clenched, and his eyes so wide open that the whites could be seen all round.

'My God, George, what is that thing?' he whispered.

'That, my dear doctor, is the result of years of experimenting. It first became visible to the naked eye five years ago today, but it does not appear to have grown during the last six months. It vindicates Crosse absolutely. Don't you think it is superb?'

'Superb? Oh, yes, it's superb!' said the doctor. He kept muttering to himself as he walked round the table, glaring at the thing on it, but from the few words I caught he was not calling it superb or anything like it.

At last his love of biology overcame his repugnance.

'I should like to feel one of those filaments,' he said, and stretched out his hand.

Like a flash of lightning Vickers seized his wrist, and his face was the colour of chalk. Dr Vane looked astonished and hurt.

'I am sorry, doctor, but I forgot to tell you it can give a terrific electric shock,' he said apologetically.

Vane looked somewhat scared, but his interest was plainly increased.

'Then it is some sort of relation to the Gymnotus, or electric eel of Venezuela?' he asked.

'Or the Torpedo of the Mediterranean,' I suggested.

Vickers shrugged his shoulders.

'I only know that poor old Tippoo' — a splendid collie and great favourite of us all — 'happened to accompany me to this room yesterday, and poked his nose a bit too near, when he suddenly toppled over dead as a doornail. He was horribly burnt down one side.'

Our friend spoke quietly, but it was easy to see he was deeply affected as he related the tragedy.

'That must have startled you,' I said.

'Well, no, I cannot say it was a surprise. I received a very nasty shock when it was quite small — perhaps I was not handling it as carefully as I might have. But' — here he turned to that monstrous creature, and actually passed his hand down one of its hairy legs — 'but you know who feeds you, don't you, my beauty?'

The thing evidently did know, for that trunk-like object went in and out rapidly. And I might say here that was the only movement we noticed in it that evening.

The startled look on our faces seemed to amuse Vickers.

'It's all right; it knows me. I have watched it grow day by day, and — '

Here the doctor cut in with a question.

'What do you feed the brute on?' he asked.

Vickers hesitated a moment, and looked at us. Then he walked to the other side of the room, and opened a box which had airholes pierced in it.

'The trunk,' he explained, 'is fitted with two small pointed teeth at the end, and the blood of the victim is gradually sucked out.' He anticipated our next question. 'No. It does not kill it first,' he said, and shut the lid.

The box contained live mice.

It was exactly ten days later that I was sitting with Vane in his study over a game of chess. At least, we were supposed to be playing chess. As a matter of fact, the doctor was again telling me what he thought of our friend's experiment, and the game had languished.

'I tell you it's the greatest discovery ever made — the greatest!' And his fist thumped the table, making the pieces on the board dance again. His eyes shone with excitement, but this died away as his thoughts travelled in a different channel. 'But of all the ugly things God every created — '

He stopped abruptly.

'Do you know,' he continued presently, 'that Vickers's interesting pet belongs to the family of mites — ticks, as they are popularly called — notwithstanding its extraordinary size? All these creatures are furnished with suckers through which they can draw the juices of the animals on which they are parasitic, and in tropical countries — well, I will just say they are considerably more than annoying, and leave the rest to your imagination. They are small and flat when they first settle themselves on their victim, but they gradually swell and redden, until at last, when they are fully gorged, they are as large as broad-beans, and as easily crushed as ripe gooseberries.

'It seems to me from its mode of formation that George has discovered the link between the inorganic world and the world of life — the link which is indispensable to a complete scheme of evolution; but the great objection to this idea is the creature's obvious complexity — '

My further remarks were interrupted by a knock at the door, and the doctor's maid Emily entered.

'Mr Vickers's housekeeper would like to speak to you, sir.'

I heard Vane's 'Ah!' although it was said very softly. I remember my heart was beating at a ridiculous rate, and I tried hard to calm myself as I reflected that probably the old lady had come about her 'screws,' as she called her rheumatism, and which I knew had been troubling her more than usual.

But Dr Vane went down the two flights of stairs to his surgery two steps at a time. At the door he turned round and simply nodded to me, and we entered together.

Mrs Jones, Vickers's housekeeper, was waiting, with her veil pushed up until it looked like a black bandage across her forehead.

'Is it Mr Vickers?' Vane asked abruptly.

Mrs Jones never spoke quickly, and she did not intend to be hurried that day. Her reply came slowly, so deliberately that I thought my supply of patience would ebb away long before that simple question was answered.

'Well, sir, I don't know as there is anything the matter with Mr Vickers, but he ain't had a bite since one o'clock yesterday, and yet I feel certain as he is in the house. He went upstairs — '

I think Mrs Jones had reason to look astonished, for Dr Vane, noted for his precise ways and highly professional manner, dashed to the house-telephone and shouted into

the mouthpiece: 'Tell John to bring the car round at once!
You understand? He is not to delay one moment!' Then he
turned to the housekeeper, who stood with her mouth half
open, and said rapidly: 'You will come with us, and give us
further particulars on the road.'

What had happened? I dreaded to think of what that
upstairs room would reveal to us. The doctor and I looked
at each other. Then he placed his hand on my arm.

'Charlie,' he whispered, 'you can depend on it George has
got foul of that monster. I have felt something would
happen, ever since he showed it to us, and it looks very
much as if that something has happened.'

'I pray God we shall not be too late!' I said fervently, but I
thought of that Thing, with the never-winking eyes, and
shuddered.

'Have you a revolver?' I asked.

He nodded, and left the surgery.

A few moments later the motor arrived. We bundled Mrs
Jones in; and as Vane gave the chauffeur the address, he
added: 'Drive like hell!' I shall not forget that ride in a
hurry, and I am quite sure Mrs Jones won't. We plied her
with questions, but her replies were so incoherent we soon
gave it up. She sat with bulging eyes, one hand clutching the
side of the car, the other my coat, and every time it bumped
over an obstacle she shrieked. More than once I bawled into
her ear: 'It's all right!' but I might have saved my breath,
for she made no sort of variation on her terror-stricken cry:
'Stop it! Stop it!'

A scared-looking maid let us in. We brushed past her,
and went straight upstairs. Arriving at the door of that
room, we stopped and listened, but could detect not the
slightest sound. We tried the door — it was locked. So, after
all that tearing hurry we were met by a well-built door, and
Vickers had the key. We looked at each other in despair, but
with Dr Vane it lasted but a moment, and was succeeded by
a look of grim determination.

'He is in there, and we have got to get to him,' he said
decisively.

'I'll fetch a locksmith: I think that will turn out to be the
quickest way out of the difficulty,' I said, and was on the

point of moving off when the doctor whispered excitedly: 'Wait! Listen! He is speaking!'

I tiptoed back to the door, and listened with loudly beating heart, but hardly breathing: there was silence, a long silence, then I heard a voice, but what it said I could not distinguish. It seemed to come from afar off, like a voice on a telephone that had been badly connected up. Vane shook his head.

'Speak up, old man! We can't hear you!' he shouted.

Again we listened, and this time we could just make out the words '... key ... false ... bottom ... desk,' then all was quiet again.

'Which drawer, and how do you open it?' the doctor asked loudly. But not another sound came from the room, although he repeated the question twice.

Vane turned to me. 'That's a piece of luck. I wonder why he had two keys made? Well, we have got to find that duplicate, quick,' he said.

We rapidly made our way to Vickers's study, where we knew there was a roller-top desk. We thanked Heaven when we found the door open, and also the desk. It was a beautiful piece of furniture, and the top was rolled back, showing the row of pigeon-holes and small drawers. Tucked in one of the pigeon-holes was a bunch of keys.

'Now, where the dickens is the drawer with the false bottom?' said Vane, and he hurriedly tried to find the keys which fitted the drawers.

Now, investigations of this sort cannot be hurried, and, swearing softly, he demonstrated this fact completely. The swearing grew louder and louder, till, for a moment, I lost sight of the object of the search in amazement at the extent of his vocabulary.

I relieved him of the bunch when he had opened half the drawers. Eventually we unlocked the lot, but although we quickly took a large number of measurements, we could not find the slightest indication of a false bottom to any of them.

Our nerves were in a high state of tension before we entered the study; by this time, mine were in a deplorable condition. The doctor's face was lined with anxiety.

Silently he handed me a poker, and from the wall took down an old Malay kriss, which did duty for an ornament.

'You take the right side of the desk; I'll take the other,' I said.

We found the precious key, but the desk —

Again we were at the door upstairs, and, although I turned the lock, I dreaded pushing it open. The whole business was so uncanny. Was that horrible creature prowling about the room ready to rush at us the moment we entered? How should we find Vickers?

I glanced at Vane. His jaw was set, and he had taken the revolver out of his pocket. The only sounds we could hear were some carts rumbling along the roadway, and the whistling from a train a long way off.

But the business in hand was very real and desperately urgent, and I do not think anyone would have noticed any hesitancy in pushing that door open; yet the next moment we were suddenly struck motionless as a low whisper reached us: 'For God's sake, move as quietly as you can!' We entered on tiptoe.

There are some scenes which are stamped on the memory in such a way that they are never forgotten. Years after they can be called to the eye of the mind with wonderful fidelity to detail. The scene which met us was such a one.

A broad beam from the setting sun came through the bottom of one of the windows, where the blind had not been completely drawn, and we saw. Very plainly, too, for the beam fell straight on it.

Vickers lay stretched on his back in the middle of the room, with that grisly Thing straddled across his chest, its sucker buried in his throat. His face and lips were quite bloodless. His eyes were closed, and I could detect no sort of movement.

I looked at Vane. His brows were contracted till they almost met, and his breath came and went through his teeth with a little hissing noise. I reminded him of the revolver ready cocked in his hand.

'Don't be a fool!' he said irritably. 'Get some brandy, and, for Heaven's sake, look slippy!'

When I returned he had his fingers on the poor fellow's wrist, and the frown was still on his face, but the revolver was on the box which was pierced with airholes.

I suppose I must have looked puzzled. Vane spoke impatiently, yet his voice was hardly above a whisper.

'Look here: what guarantee is there I should kill this vampire before it had time to discharge its deadly current through George's body? You know as well as I do that creatures low down in the scale of creation take a lot of killing. We can't risk it, and I am sure we can't risk hauling it off.'

The brandy was doing its work, and Vickers must have heard some of our conversation, because his eyes opened, and he said, with a ghost of a smile: 'Have you ever seen a leech applied, Charlie?'

I started violently.

'Good heavens! you don't mean to say Vane and I have to hang about with our hands in our pockets doing nothing except speculating whether — whether — '

'Whether I shall be able to stand the drain till it shifts?'

Vickers smiled again as he took the words out of my mouth.

The thought was intolerable; surely there must be some way!

For hours Vane sat waiting. I also was waiting, but on a couch in another room, getting over the effects of a little blood transfusion. 'It is very necessary,' Vane had said, as he skilfully made the arrangements, so skilfully that the creature was not disturbed. The improved appearance of poor George was my reward.

Wearied in mind and body I fell asleep, and dreamed dreams of men and women I knew, but I gazed at them with horror, for they all had drawn, blanched faces, with great staring eyes, and something with its body across their chests and with head buried at their throats, and they beseeched me by all I held sacred to take it from them, but I was bound by invisible bands. How shall I tell of my agony of mind? I woke with a start, and in a terrible perspiration, and found the doctor looking at me, hollow-eyed and unshaved.

162

'Nightmare?' he asked. 'Where did you want to go, and who wouldn't let you? Steady, steady,' he added, as I jumped up and swayed, owing to the floor apparently moving about. As he pointed out, transfusion has no great tendency to make things appear as steady as rocks.

'Has the thing moved?' I asked.

'No,' he answered laconically.

We looked at each other in silence. I was hoping he would guess my next question, but I had to ask it.

'How is George?'

'Alive.' And I knew from the way he said it that he had told me simply the bare truth and that was all. There was another long silence.

'Oh! can't we do something?' I cried despairingly.

'Yes,' replied Vane. 'I am going to do something if that vampire does not move in ten minutes. The point has been reached when the risk is negligible, inasmuch as if it does not move now there will be no necessity of doing anything. I am going to shoot it.'

We returned to that chamber of horrors. Poor Vickers looked ghastly, and it did not require a trained eye to see that the end was not far off.

I took my watch out. 'Give it five minutes,' muttered Vane; and I sat on the box with the airholes, glancing first at the deathlike face of Vickers, then at Vane's set features as he stood stroking his unshaven chin, gazing at our friend.

'Time's up,' I said.

The doctor walked gently till he was opposite the creature's head, and droped on one knee, then lowered the revolver till it was within six inches of its head. His finger was on the trigger when a strange thing occurred: the bloated monster suddenly withdrew its sucker and glared at him as if it knew that its hour of death had arrived. I thought Vane was fascinated by those baleful eyes, for he did not stir as the creature commenced to move towards him.

'Look out!' I shouted, and he sprang back. None too soon, for the thing rushed at him with incredible swiftness.

Then I had an opportunity of witnessing Vane's beautiful nerve, for not until the last trailing filament had left Vickers did he fire. I saw his finger press the trigger. The next instant a terrific report shook the building, and my hands flew up to my eyes to shut out that terrible blinding flash. Women's screams, mingled with noises as if giant hands were tearing the house to pieces, floated up from below.

The sound of someone groaning made me rouse myself.

Vane lay face downwards in an immense pool of blood, his head hanging over a ragged hole in the floor. I thanked Heaven fervently when I found that he had only been stunned by the vast charge of static electricity the creature had suddenly let loose. Like a flash of lightning the charge had struck the floor, bursting it open, then torn its way through the house.

We turned to Vickers. Vane felt his pulse.

'I will save him,' he said. And he did.

Bibliography

Blackwood's Magazine 'Letter to Eusebius About Many Things' John
     Eagles (January 1853).
'Book of Days' Robert Chambers (1864).
British Quarterly Review 'Andrew Crosse' (October 1859).
'Dictionary of National Biography' L. Stephen (Vol XIII).
'Elements of Electricity and Electro-Chemistry' George J. Singer
     (1814).
'A History of the Thirty Years Peace' Harriet Martineau (1846).
'The Land of Quantock' Rev William Greswell (1918).
'Lectures on Electricity' Henry M. Noad (1849).
'The Life & Letters of Mary Wollstonecraft Shelley' Mrs Julian
     Marshall (1889).
'The Life of Percy Bysshe Shelley' Thomas Medwin. Ed. H. B.
     Forman (1913).
'Local Traditions of the Quantocks' Rev C. W. Whistler (1908).
'Memorials Scientific and Literary of Andrew Crosse' Cornelia
     Crosse (1857).
'Oddities' Rupert T. Gould (1928).
'Proceedings of the British Association' Reports for 1825 and 1854.
'Quantock Country' Berta Lawrence (1952).
'Quantock Life and Rambles' Rev Edward H. Smith (1945).
'Red Letter Days of My Life' Cornelia Crosse (1892).
'Shelley' Newman I. White (1947).
'Southey' Jack Simmons (1945).
'Stranger Than Science' Frank Edwards (1959).
'Students Text-Book of Electricity' Henry M. Noad and W. H.
     Preece (1855).

'Transactions of the London Electrical Society' (1838).
'Unsolved Mysteries' Valentine Dyall (1954).

I have also extensively consulted the files of the following newspapers, *The Times*, *The Western Gazette*, *Somerset County Gazette*, *Taunton Courier*, *Bridgwater Mercury* and the *West Somerset Free Press*.

By way of acknowledgement I should like to thank the staffs of the Bridgwater Public Library, The British Museum and the London Library for their help in locating material; Bill Lofts for his assistance with the research; and Joe Chamberlaine who took the photographs for this book of the various localities in Broomfield as they are today. And last, but by no means least, Pam Chamberlaine who sustained me through the whole operation with the best baked jam rolls in the South West!